C000205785

SUNBATHING NAKED
AND OTHER MIRACLE CURES

Also by Guy Kennaway

One People (fiction)
I Can Feel It Moving (fiction)
The Winner of the Fooker Prize (fiction)

SUNBATHING NAKED
AND OTHER MIRACLE CURES

A MEMOIR BY GUY KENNAWAY

CANONGATE

Edinburgh · London · New York · Melbourne

First published in Great Britain in 2008 by
Canongate Books Ltd, 14 High Street,
Edinburgh EH1 1TE

1

Copyright © Guy Kennaway, 2008

The moral right of the author has been asserted

Every effort has been made to trace copyright holders and to obtain their
permission for the use of copyright material. The publisher apologises for
any errors or omissions in the following list and would be grateful if notified
of any corrections that should be incorporated in future reprints or editions
of this book.

'Sledgehammer' lyrics reproduced by permission of Peter Gabriel and Real
World Music Publishing.

'(Sexual) Healing' words and music by Marvin Gaye, David Ritz and Odell
Brown, © 1982, EMI April Music Inc/Ritz Writes/EMI Blackwood Music
Inc, USA. Reproduced by permission of EMI Songs Ltd, London W8 5SW.

On Beauty copyright © Zadie Smith, 2005 (Hamish Hamilton). Reproduced
by permission.

'Missing' lyrics by Ben Watt and Tracey Thorn © Sony/ATV Music
Publishing. All rights reserved. Reproduced by permission.

'New York, New York' words by Fred Ebb and music by John Kander
© 1977 EMI Unart Catalog Inc and EMI United Partnership Ltd.
EMI United Partnership Ltd (publishing) and Alfred Publishing Co (print).
Administered in Europe by Faber Music Ltd. All rights reserved.

'1st World Psoriasis Day, 24 October 2004: New International Survey Shows
People with Psoriasis Continue to be Rejected by Others' (distributed on
the net by PR Newswire) excerpt reproduced by permission of the
International Federation of Psoriasis Associations.

Now magazine excerpt reproduced by permission.

British Library Cataloguing-in-Publication Data
A catalogue record for this book is available on
request from the British Library

ISBN 978 1 84767 045 8

Typeset by Palimpsest Book Production Limited,Grangemouth, Stirlingshire
Printed and bound in Great Britain by MacKays of Chatham
This book is printed on FSC certified paper

Mixed Sources
Product group from well-managed
forests and other controlled sources
www.fsc.org Cert no. TT-COC-002341
© 1996 Forest Stewardship Council
FSC

Contents

Part 2

Part 1

1
My Companion

My sister was born with a birthmark on her right cheek. A bluey-brown blob, slightly raised. In my family this was considered a blessing. Four years younger than her, I gazed at it with envy. I saw that strangers noticed it straight away, but interpreted their alarm (recoiling, eyes darting away, pretending not to notice) as stunned admiration. This was because my mum (brown hair, pale soft skin liable to blushing and blotching) had informed us that Emma's birthmark 'made her more attractive' and gave her face 'character' – apparently a very good thing. All I had was a bit of eczema on my elbow and a little scab I kept going for years on my nose because I thought it too made me more attractive. Because we were home-schooled and had little contact with the outside world, my mum managed to maintain this heroic act of offspring protection. But there was some corroborating evidence: I heard people call it a strawberry birthmark – and everyone knew that strawberries were good.

There were a lot of things that were clearly established by my mother which wouldn't have stood the most cursory check against reality. For instance, she informed us that our dad (thick black hair, dark skin that went brown easily and stubble like a suede brush) was the best father and husband in the world, despite the fact that he rarely showed up at home and when he did, had the appearance of a man with something rather more interesting on his mind. She also informed us that we were aristocrats, despite the fact that my grandparents were shopkeepers – not exactly a blue-blooded calling. So the small matter of denying the effects of a birthmark presented no difficulty to my mum, and the subject, once settled, was no longer discussed.

Only when Emma went to school did it dawn on me that the rest of the world didn't understand how wonderful her facial disfigurement was. When an enterprising film-maker came looking for children for a Smarties advert he chose the entire school, with one exception: my sister. I remember seeing Emma watching the Smarties ad on TV featuring all her school friends – pink blemishless skins, sparkling eyes – scoffing Smarties, and thinking, There's something not quite right here.

Her original birthmark remains only in my memory because not a single photograph exists of her prior to her visit to hospital to get it dealt with. Naturally, my mum was hiding all kinds of fears and anxieties behind her declaration that there wasn't a problem with Emma's face, and she wanted to get the birthmark fixed. It's now called plastic surgery, though what happened to my sister in the mid-1950s is better described as wooden. They cut and tugged flaps of skin over the birthmark and sewed them into a Y, which is now clearly printed on her upper cheek, though they missed a bit and left an island of dark blue from her cheekbone to her hairline.

Once my mum had established that the surgeon's scar made Emma 'even more attractive', and 'added more character', debate on the subject was again dropped. This was the manner of our family; even when something was as plain as the nose on your face, or plainer as in Emma's case, it could be denied

4

out of existence. The Kennaway first aid box was empty but for a bit of paper that said, 'STOP FUSSING AND GET ON WITH IT'. So when it dawned on me that everybody else in the world held different opinions on the subject of skin problems, I drew the inevitable conclusion: they must be wrong.

Later I discovered that my mother's own mother – who had soft wrinkled white skin with pale moles – hid ghastly scars under her clothes, horrific burns from when her dress caught fire in her thirties. Concealment was the strategy she taught my mum, and concealment was the technique I learnt at my mother's knee. If our skin is the point at which we meet the world, then my mum was the skin of our family – absorbing the blows dealt by reality while wrapping us in her protective layer.

When I developed a rash on my face in my mid-twenties, I had no idea of the hell I was descending into. On first seeing the red blotches around my mouth and nostrils, I took the family line and simply denied anything was wrong. I declared that they were 'a shaving rash'. Sounded manly and, I hoped, almost enviable, the consequence of my virility and hirsuteness being that I had to shave particularly roughly and toughly.

Treatment was sponging my face in scalding water. I had been brought up to think of my body as something to be bashed and punished into obedience. The marks – red patches no bigger than postage stamps – came and went of their own accord; I didn't like them, but I began to accommodate them in my life. I certainly didn't want to subject my skin to the scrutiny of a doctor. My father had a succession of heart attacks and treated them all with a stiff glass of whisky, a Player's cigarette and an early night. He died young, at a hundred and ten. Or at least that was the speed he was doing when he hit the Armco barrier on the M4 after his final heart attack. He was forty years old.

The stuff on my face was quick to establish itself in my life, providing a commentary on all my activities. Some things I did, like drink heavy red wine and party late into the night, it disapproved of, and it would be waiting in the morning to reprove me at its most blotchy. But it wasn't just a party-pooping bore. Another long night on the Scotch could result in a clear complexion the next day. Above all it wasn't predictable, although I never gave up trying to second-guess it. It seemed to have a preference for some of my friends over others, appearing all over my face and neck, bright red, almost pulsing with rage, in the pub with some, and calmly disappearing entirely with the departure – or arrival – of others. And it wasn't as if it was warning me to stay away from bad apples. I had lots of gloriously ill-behaved friends to whom it was happy to let me present a clear complexion, and other exemplary characters, like a university tutor – a lovely pink-skinned, bald-headed, laconic and amusing southern American – to whom it always reacted violently.

I often tried to make a list of its dislikes: the barber, the dentist, my mother, cheap red wine, but apart from those four regulars, the rest of the list needed constant revision. Each day of my diary I gave my skin a score out of ten, 0 being clear and 10 being encrusted in angry red blotches, hoping I could look back and find a pattern that would unlock the secret. I've just flicked through the years 1982 and 1983. Weeks go by without a number on the top of the page – I must have given up the task, or thought it had gone for good – but then it reappears.

Here's a typical entry:

3. Only a little rawness around my left nostril, tiny bit of peeling on my chin – otherwise clear . . . 7 p.m. 9 after getting on the phone and arranging to meet K and D for a meal at the Café Roma. Big peelings either side of nostrils, red left eye – aargh, never been in the eye before. Corner of mouth bad. Tip of nose like some kind of danger beacon. Fuck. Cancelled supper. Bit of an improvement immediately.

I spent a lot of time in cinemas. I was living in Edinburgh, which is well served by cinemas, including the Dominion, a lovely old-fashioned one far from the city centre in a tree-lined suburban street where I could sit and while away an afternoon in the company of other people who also couldn't quite face life in the light for one reason or another.

I was quick to notice how unblemished the complexions projected on to the screen were. Few spots, rashes, scabs or rawness of any kind appear in films. And the same goes for magazines. I trembled to think of how my face would look enlarged to twenty feet, when the magnifying mirror on its concertina fixing in my mother's bathroom was an instrument of torture for me.

There's a man called Vail Reese, who lives in the US, who has a website called skinema.com devoted entirely to the subject of skin 'disorders' in the movies (it was only a matter of time before somebody challenged that word with quotation marks). He combs every film for zits and hives. Obsessive? A bit, but that I am afraid is the hallmark of somebody suffering from a skin 'disorder' himself. Vail delights in featuring stills of big movie stars – including Brad Pitt, Angelina Jolie and Leonardo

DiCaprio – with their acne allegedly pressing through layers of make-up. Almost no great star escapes some kind of diagnosis. His general message is don't worry about bad skin, the most beautiful people in the world have it.

But Vail wouldn't be Vail if he stopped there; he has also analysed the rare occasions when bad skin is visible in movies. And his conclusion? That it always signifies internal badness. For instance, Vail has discovered that *Star Trek* villains have way above average incidence of psoriasis, eczema, fungi and other assorted skin ailments. It's surprising there wasn't a dermatologist on the *Enterprise*. I can see Vail now, his own skin red and scabby, as he sits with his clipboard in front of the TV, at his feet the open *Star Trek* box sets. Like me – like all of us with 'bad skin' – he's just trying to make sense of what's going on, and like the rest of us it's sent him a bit nutty.

If we turn off the TV and pick up a book, the same awful message is there. Bad skin equals bad person. Why did Ian Fleming never give Bond a dose of cold sores? The question goes deep. With Bond's lifestyle there are few men less likely to escape them. Even Zadie Smith, that champion of oppressed minorities, gives us a kicking. In *On Beauty,* Bailey, the boss of Tower Records in Boston and a tedious sex pest, has 'skin on his hand [that] peeled and bled, the worst example of the psoriasis that also showed up in milder patches on his neck and forehead'. And one hundred and seven pages later, when the hero Howard takes the hand of his old father Harold – who is the book's only out and out racist bigot – guess what? 'He felt the little rough patches of psoriasis.'

*   *   *

My bad skin became my companion and like most friendships we had our ups and downs. I often hated it, and was furious with the way it made me look so crusty and red, and made me withdraw from so many things I wanted to do, but then at other times, when my face magically cleared, and I looked into the mirror to see my eyes and nose and mouth rather than just a collection of nasty peeling red patches, I was so thankful to it, and felt a great surge of love for my friend, my merciful skin. Okay, I admit it: I was caught in an abusive relationship, but when you are in one of these things it's so hard to see it, and to understand what a prat you are for sticking around . . . But of course that was the difference: I couldn't leave my abusive relationship. Short of searing my face with a blow torch (and I know someone who was so despairing they tried to do just that), I am stuck with it and stuck in it. I can't leave.

It has guided me through life and made many choices for me. It kept me from the beach and from swimming – both of which I had loved as child – and made me instead take up scuba diving with its concealing rubber suit and mask. It led me towards the only other sport where I could comprehensively hide my skin with masks and goggles and gloves without attracting any attention: skiing, for which I thank it. It kept me away from job interviews, romantic dinners, over-lit rooms and anything to do with cameras. The one time I went on TV I blushed and blotched so much I felt like my skin was on fire and was desperate to get out from under the searing gaze of that black rectangle of glass. I wonder if Vail, with his network of informants, has logged my appearance on one of his charts.

It gave me a tendency towards white or pale clothes,

which hide flakes of skin, when I much prefer to dress in dark ones. I was drawn towards other people with bad skin, out of sheer sympathy with their pain, and eventually married a woman who had suffered from acne. It forbade me to work in sales or even amongst other people in an office, so I was led to that most solitary of professions: writing. I do not know if I would have done this were it not for my bad skin, but I know I'd rather be stared at by an empty page than a stranger.

I have had to live in a world which thinks that people get the skin they deserve. When Jeffrey Archer was on trial for perjury it was gleefully reported that he had broken out in psoriasis. The word always leaps out at me from the newspaper. Jeffrey's condition (I nearly wrote 'poor Jeffrey's condition') was presented by the tabloids as the inevitable consequence of simply being Jeffrey Archer, and by the broadsheets as the truth seeping through his skin no matter how hard he tried to hide it.

People do not get the skin they deserve. I have seen too many children with horrific afflictions to entertain that notion for a moment. I have seen parents whose lives have been savaged trying to raise a child with really bad skin. It sent my acquaintance Bill bonkers. He is a big podgy Canadian guy with a black greasy fringe and milky skin. His daughter Emily, who was nine when she was first hit, had a body patterned with plaques of scaly red flaky psoriasis the size of dinner plates. When it started spreading its thick carapace up her neck towards her face, Bill decided that the only thing to do was convert the entire family to Islam so Emily could walk around with her face hidden under a burka.

'It's got to be ultra-hardcore Islam,' Bill sighed, sweating with a combination of fear and love for Emily, who was in the next room with her mother Marie, 'like the Taliban, so she can wear one of those postboxes with a blue mesh over it.'

'Bill,' I said, 'that's madness. You can't do that . . .' (he was Jewish for a start).

His hands gripped into the fat on his knees and his whole body shook with despair. Tears trickled from his eyes and through clenched teeth, because he didn't want Marie or Emily to hear, he said, 'But we've tried everything . . . everything . . . We've tried every fucking cream and pill and doctor and specialist, there's nothing else . . . nothing, no one, nobody to help her, for fuck's sake . . . What am I going to do?'

Emily's skin had driven Bill mad, though fortunately conversion to ultra-orthodox Islam was not in the psoriasis's plans. I met Bill, Emily and Marie Woodward at one of the many clinics which advertise therapies that can cure us. I listened to their war stories of the fight they waged against Emily's tormentor, and was actually present at the moment the disease broke Bill's will, finally crushed him, got him to the point where he gave up and admitted he couldn't do anything to save his daughter. I don't know where they are now, or how Emily is, but I will never forget when our bitter roads briefly crossed.

We struggle on in an indifferent world. I cannot see a wheel-chair ramp without feeling the injustice of it. Why should wheelchair users get automatic wide doors and buses with lifts when none of our needs are met? We demand jars of mois-turisers positioned in all public buildings, and the removal and destruction of all public mirrors.

I had planned to write a genre novel, a crime thriller that flew off the shelves. I needed a villain that was repellent and attractive in equal measure, someone really slimy, and decided to base him on my skin disease – I was going to make him a charming sadist: cunning, playful, clever and cruel. Then I realised that writing a thriller meant I'd have to do some research into the world of criminals and cops, a milieu I knew nothing about. And this would inevitably mean coming face to face with a lot of strangers, and that thought sent something tingling through my body like iron filings along my bloodstream, and in seconds my right cheek began to smart. It was a clear message from the boss – don't go there.

So I shall write a book without cops or robbers, but keep my villain. I'll write the biography of my skin disease. After all, it's staring me in the face.

I will tell the whole story of psoriasis as I know it; I will expose its evil tricks, detail its unfathomable powers, describe it in its moods and phases, and reveal what life is like for its victims. I will explain how it drew my life to a standstill, how it miraculously seemed to disappear, and then when I finally thought I'd seen the last of it, how it morphed into a creepy new form which sent me mad and brought me demented to the gates of a Category One State Mental Institution in Arizona.

But first, some history.

2

The Secret History of Psoriasis

The Hebrew word for psoriasis is *tzaraath*; it crops up frequently in the Bible, usually mistranslated as leprosy. There wasn't an English word for psoriasis until the nineteenth century, and of course leprosy, which is contagious and can kill, makes for a better story than the relatively inoffensive psoriasis. *Tzaraath* literally means 'erupt', or 'become disfigured' (a reasonable description of psoriasis) and does not in any way describe leprosy (or Hansen's disease as it's now properly called), whose two salient symptoms are nosebleeds and loss of feeling through damaged nerve endings. Hansen's disease is also very rare, affecting around 0.01 per cent of the population, making psoriasis, at 2 per cent, 200 times more likely to be the disease referred to by the writers of the Bible when they used the word *tzaraath*.

Even the most cursory examination of the stories about *tzaraath* makes it obvious it must be referring – in the main – to psoriasis. Naaman, in the second Book of Kings, was 'a valiant soldier'. Not with leprosy he wasn't. He wouldn't even be able to feel his sword in his hand. A servant girl in his house said she knew a man in Israel who could cure him – familiar words to all of us who have psoriasis. There's always some well-intentioned but essentially interfering stranger who has a story of some cure or other, often abroad, and usually expensive. The best way to deal with them is to say you're happy with the way you look.

Naturally when Naaman went to this 'healer' he took with him that which we all know he'd need a lot of: cash. 'Ten talents of silver and six thousand shekels of gold', to be precise. When Naaman reached the healer, who was called Elisha, Elisha sent out a messenger to treat him.

Like most dermatologists, Elisha was too busy to see him without an appointment. The messenger said, 'Go wash yourself seven times in the Jordan, and your flesh will be restored and you will be cleansed.' This sounds exactly like the kind of weird alternative therapy we psoriatics are familiar with. I have lain in mud, I've inhaled the most filthy Chinese herbs, I've used bright yellow suppositories, I've even smeared my face with rotting mushrooms, so seven dips in a river is fairly standard.

Naaman, however, complained to the messenger, '"I thought he [Elisha] would surely come out to me and stand and call on the name of the Lord, wave his hand over the spot and cure me of my *tzaraath*,"' he said. 'And he turned and went off in a rage.'

Two things arise: first, he clearly says 'spot'. That's psoriasis. Hansen's disease affects large areas of skin not with spots but with heavy slack wrinkles, which later pit with boils. Psoriasis always starts as red *spots*, which then ripen into silvery scabs. The second thing is the speed with which Naaman rises to rage. The anger at daily examining and then re-examining our reflections, charting the ups and downs of our utterly unpredictable condition, keeps us constantly simmering with rage and liable to throw a hissy fit at the slightest setback.

A verse or two later Naaman does go and dip in the river, and lo and behold: 'His flesh was restored and became clean like that of a young boy.' This is exactly the kind of inexplicable remission that psoriasis – unlike leprosy – is prone to. Not that it makes it any less of a miracle. It *is* miraculous when it suddenly clears; I always feel like dropping to my knees and singing praises to God. But usually I'm in too much of a hurry to go out and enjoy myself.

Having been 'cured', Naaman does a very psoriatic thing: he loads his mules with as much earth as they can carry so he can worship the Lord on Israeli soil when he's back at home. How common it is for us to go berserk when we think we have found a cure for our psoriasis. Emily, the nine-year-old Canadian, went into remission after coincidentally (we now know) eating a meal of pomegranates when abroad. For the next three months her dad Bill must have imported about ten kilos of Mexican pomegranates and almost force-fed them to his daughter. The psoriasis defiantly, disdainfully and arrogantly reappeared on her body worse than ever.

For hundreds, if not thousands, of years psoriatics were literally considered lepers, and this was in the days when they treated a leper like a leper, which meant we were parted from our wives, husbands, children and friends, exiled from society and forced to rot in a colony for the rest of our lives.

Treatment of psoriasis was not sophisticated. That medical textbook of the Old Testament, known as Leviticus, which recommends many herbal cures for other diseases, prescribes only one for psoriatics: straight banishment. And while banished the psoriatic had to 'wear torn clothes, let his head hang loose, cover his upper lip and cry, "Unclean!"' It's clear that most of this is skinist (I need the word, so must invent it) bigotry and hatred, but I cannot see why they wanted the upper lip to be covered, nor how this was to be accomplished.

Herodotus records that there were many leper colonies in Egypt, but once again it's unlikely that the occupants suffered from anything more serious than psoriasis – to repeat, not a contagious disease – for, despite testing thousands of Egyptian mummies, archaeologists have not found a single case of leprosy amongst the ancient bones. (Tests for psoriasis in human remains have not been developed. This doesn't surprise me – it's just another example of the condition's evasive nature.)

Debate exists over the conditions inside the leper colonies, but, let's face it, they must have been bloody grim. Certain historians – who do not have psoriasis, I venture to suggest – have claimed that happy, functioning and thriving communities existed in these places. There are definitely stories about people faking leprosy in order to get in; hard to believe when apart from the torn clothes, forced abortion, sterilisation and in many cases 'post-partum abortion', i.e. infanticide, were standard practice.

It's more likely that when people found psoriatics who were in remission within the colonies they jumped to the conclusion that they must have been 'normal' people who had chosen to go in and join the lepers. Either that or they were just easily bullied people who were thrown on the social scrapheap known as a leper colony and then explained away as having chosen to go in by their own accord – or, and this theory I love, they were regular people who were so disgusted by the way the town treated the entirely harmless psoriatics, they could no longer stick life amongst the bigots within the city walls and went out of solidarity to join the skin people in the colony.

In Japanese leper colonies the Government murdered babies

up until the 1950s, for, apparently, their own good. Stories of happy colonies persist, it's true, but we have learnt how to make the best of a bad situation, although pretending that we liked being banished to places like Robben Island, which in the 1800s doubled as a leper colony and an open lunatic asylum, is the kind of nonsense we are quite familiar with from people with so-called 'normal' skin.

The Old Testament may be short on cures, but it's long on causes of psoriasis, and it carefully lists them in Leviticus:

Gossiping
Murder
Making a vain oath
Having illicit sexual intercourse
Pride
Theft
Stinginess

With the exception of the murder (up till the point of writing) it's me to a T, though I don't think there is a psoriatic character. That idea is a malicious skinist proposition, an excuse to point at someone with red splodges on the neck, arms and head and say, 'See − a thieving sex-mad murderer.'

In time, treatments were developed by the kind and thoughtful 'smoothies' for us psoriasis sufferers. Here is a list:

Cat faeces (Ancient Egypt)
Onions, sea salt and urine (I'm not sure if that's three 'cures' or one. Germany, thirteenth century.)
Goose-oil and semen (You could sell that now as a £400-a-pot moisturiser in Los Angeles. France.)

Wasp droppings in sycamore milk (Both readily available at all branches of Boots. Italy.)
Soup made from vipers (Make it easy for us, won't you? Germany.)
Arsenic (Britain, nineteenth and twentieth centuries – when they learnt to cut to the chase and just kill us for having dry skin.)

You can't really call them cures, more punishments. They certainly throw more light on the prevailing mood of the era than they do on psoriasis. But that is a characteristic of the disease – it has a way of holding up a mirror to the time and to the patient.

Finally, in Vienna in the nineteenth century psoriasis was given its own name, by a man called Ferdinand von Hebron, the etymology of which is Greek, *psorian*, meaning itch, related to *psen*, meaning scratch, rake and reduce to dust (thought to be a reference to our souls). It's a good word for the condition, psoriasis. With its silent P and evasive, slippery vowels it summons the cunning and cleverness of the disease that is the master of disguise.

3
Diagnosis

Claire and Gemma

I met Claire, a large jolly woman who ran a rare-breeds farm in Gloucestershire, in a dermatologist's waiting room in the early 1990s. She was then about forty, and had had psoriasis since her mid-twenties. She told me that when she had first gone to her GP he had told her that the coin-sized plaques of dry skin on her buttocks and thighs were friction burns from rubbing clothes.

Of the many psoriatics I have met almost all were initially wrongly diagnosed when they peeled back their clothes and revealed their skin in a doctor's surgery. The disease has a skill for confusing its many victims – and amongst its victims I don't just include the patient, but also their friends, relatives and especially doctors.

'The doctor actually told me to wear looser clothes,' Claire told me with a booming laugh. 'Good God, any looser and I'd have had to get them made by a marquee company.'

As the marks were on her buttocks she had to make big changes in her daily life to prevent her clothes rubbing. When she fed her chickens in the early morning if it was warm enough she did it without wearing underpants or trousers. She stood in the cinema, watched TV leaning against the wall and ate on her feet with a plate in her hand.

'It's a bit like having extremely troublesome piles,' she told her friend Oliver 'Thicket' Muston-Clive. Not that she shared her predicament widely. Thicket was a confidant.

In 1995, Claire fell in love with a man – when everybody thought she'd left it too late for that kind of thing – and started going out with him. The campaign to clear her buttocks was rejoined with fervour, as she now had a new reason to get rid of the silver-edged, coin-shaped plaques. Robert was a tall hunting man with red skin himself, though not as a consequence of a designated skin disorder but from drinking port, being rather unfit and spending a lot of time in the saddle in icy weather. Claire liked his loyal, old-fashioned style so much she quickly came to the conclusion that she wanted to marry him. She also wanted to have sex with him, but that seemed more of a problem. The skin, as a regulator of body temperature and producer of enzymes and hormones, is an organ, and in the right hands a sex organ. Psoriasis has amongst its many claims the ability to really mess with your sex life. It's as if it enjoys doing it. When it's shameful to strip off and reveal your nakedness, sex becomes a nightmare, if not totally impossible. Of course Claire was scared that if Robert saw the so-called 'garment burns' he'd run a mile. She had got no joy from the doctor's tubes of ointments, so when the moment came and she found herself in bed with Robert, she just hurriedly turned off the light and pulled up the bed covers to hide herself. It was brave of her to do even this. There are tens of thousands of skin people who have had to cut sex (with other people) out of their lives altogether because they are too scared of rejection.

'Every time Robert's hand started going near my bum,' she told me, 'I wriggled like mad so he wouldn't feel the patches,' she laughed. 'It went on for months, and, of course, I always had to walk backwards to the bathroom. One morning he asked me why I never turned my back on him in the bedroom – and I said it was because I loved him so much I couldn't take my eyes off him. He proposed a week later,' she smiled at the memory. 'I said yes of course, and then thought, Blimey, when am I going to tell him about the psoriasis? I'm marrying under false pretences . . .'

Another patient I met was called Gemma. She told me that in 1995 she was a blonde-haired happy-go-lucky fifteen-year-old GCSE student living in St George's Hill. She had also been misdiagnosed by her doctor. When little scabs appeared almost overnight on her arms and chest her mum, called Chrissie, had whisked her to the local GP who had looked her over and said that the scabs were a side effect of tonsillitis (something Gemma didn't have and hadn't had for years.)

Over the next few days the 'tonsillitis spots' persisted, without her throat getting sore, and the diagnosis was altered – by a different doctor – to chickenpox. Huge sigh of relief from all concerned. Gemma was put into quarantine in her cosy pink bedroom in her expensive suburban home and the rash, which up until then had seemed rather sinister, was no longer quite so scary now it had such an innocuous name. But she didn't feel ill, and didn't get the high temperature that the doctor had predicted.

Chrissie, an energetic and effective woman with impeccably cut, rich black hair, had driven Gemma to the health centre a week later.

'I don't know why the scabs haven't fallen off,' the young doctor, a curly-haired man with dark freckles on chubby cheeks, had admitted. 'They should be falling off by now.'

'I'm going out to a party on Friday,' said Gemma, 'They'll have gone by then, won't they?'

It was a nurse who first got it right, not that she was listened to. She had come into the surgery to pick up a prescription the previous patient had accidentally left on the desk, glanced at Gemma and just said, 'Ooh – psoriasis,' and was out the door.

'I want to take the cautious path here,' said the doctor. 'Take her home, put her back in bed, and watch her carefully.'

'What is it?' asked Gemma, 'What is it?'

'I still think it is a form of chickenpox, but my mind is open,' the doctor said as he wrote at his desk. 'Go home, rest, eat lightly and stay in bed.'

That night at seven Gemma heard a car crunching the gravel, looked out of her bedroom window and recognised Dr Waite, the senior practice doctor, a short stout man with a round nose, a ball of white hair and a waxy complexion. Gemma was panic struck – WHAT ON EARTH IS HE DOING HERE? WHAT IS WRONG WITH ME?

'Darling, Dr Waite has come to see you,' Chrissie said as the two of them came into the pinkness that was Gemma's bedroom.

Dr Waite checked Gemma's joints, felt her glands and peered down her throat.

'What do you think?' said Chrissie, trying to keep anxiety out of her voice, and thoughts of Hodgkin's disease, syphilis and AIDS out of her mind.

'This could be meningitis, I'm afraid.'

'But she's not ill,' said Chrissie. 'Wouldn't she have a high temperature?'

'I want her to go to hospital, just to be on the safe side. I'm not happy her with her staying at home. I'll call the hospital.'

They left a note for Gemma's dad on the kitchen table, wrapped Gemma up and drove over to the local A & E department. After half an hour amongst the battered and bruised of Weybridge, they were seen by a young female doctor behind a short thin curtain.

Gemma pulled up her T-shirt once again. It looked like she'd had red ink flicked at her. The doctor took a look, asked a few now-familiar questions and disappeared, leaving mother and daughter to sit for twenty minutes listening to the whimpers, tears and drunken laughter of the other patients before the swish of the curtain heralded yet another doctor, who also took a brief look at Gemma.

'This isn't meningitis. What you have is guttate psoriasis.'

'What's that?' mother and daughter asked.

'It's a skin disorder – those spots are where your skin is reproducing at a pathological rate. Most skin renews once in twenty-eight days, on those spots it's happening once every twenty-four hours. That's why they are so inflamed.'

'And can it be cured?'

'There are lots of treatments for it nowadays. I'm going to give you some ointment that should clear it up.'

'But it might come back after?' asked Gemma.

'The ointment should control it. But it may return, from time to time, during stressful periods, for instance.'

Both silently said, Thank God it isn't meningitis, but then Gemma thought, Oh. My. God. Is this for ever? It can't be for ever. I've got to look good for Friday.

She was given a tube of ointment to apply to the spots, which she clung to the way superstitious people clutch a rabbit's foot. The Friday party came – Chrissie helped her apply make-up over the spots on her neck, and although she wanted to cop off with a nice boy called Fred who made her laugh she had to keep her distance.

It took me two years before I went to a doctor. During that time I chose self-treatment of my 'shaving rash'. When I did finally see a doctor I too was misdiagnosed. I picked a private GP with soft white hair and a babyish face called William Coutt, who I argued in my addled mind would be more likely to give me good news than bad because I was paying. And I was right.

He took my face in his soft clean hands and looked at my skin with such tenderness I almost burst into tears.

'Mmm,' he murmured comfortingly. 'Is this anywhere else on your body?'

'No,' I replied, making the decision to keep quiet about the fact that I, like Gemma, looked like I'd taken a barrel of bird-shot at fifty paces down the left hand side of my body.

'This is nothing to worry about,' he reassured me, 'just a spot or two of dermatitis.' It was the first – of many – names that I was given for my skin.

'What does that mean?' I asked, as he walked back behind his leather-top desk and clicked the top off his fountain pen.

'It probably just means you are using too much soap,' his kind face crumpled into a simple smile. 'The fashion now is to bath every day, sometimes twice. Often the skin can't take it, because soap is an alkali and removes protective oils from your skin. I'm going to give you an ointment that'll help, and I suggest you stop using soap and take a shower rather than a bath. Come back and see me in a couple of weeks . . .'

I went to the chemist with Dr Coutt's prescription and watched carefully the pharmacist's expression to see if she checked out my skin after reading the prescription. She didn't.

She did give me my first tube of skin ointment, called Betnovate, a trade name for cortisone – a substance that was for the next eight years to be my constant companion. It didn't improve my skin, but it represented all the same badly needed hope that it might, and a conviction that I was now doing something serious and scientifically proven to improve my plight. The blotches on my face still came and went, and from time to time disappeared on my torso too, though I now believed it to be the cream that was making them go. When I returned to Dr Coutt I wanted to give him the good news that he had cured me, but the truth was his ointment couldn't control the 'dermatitis'.

As the months went by the condition announced its easy dominance over Betnovate, and the regime of showers did nothing but create a brown patch on the ceiling of the man who lived in the flat below me. I felt sorry for the kind doctor, and didn't want to return to his surgery to rub in his failure. To avoid seeing Dr Coutt I eked out each prescription for as long as I could, dabbing the stuff sparingly on my worst spots only when I thought I really needed to, i.e. when I felt most desperate. Each tube of Betnovate started life plump and smart with a turquoise stripe across its chest, in a cardboard box with my name on it, and ended short and stubby, its serrated top bunged up with fluff and its metal hem folded over and over, one corner oozing microscopic worms of translucent ointment through the fatigued metal which jabbed me through my trouser pocket. I always seemed to be able to squeeze one last bit out of the top, to put off having to go back for a morale-sapping inspection by Dr Coutt, though after a year I gave up seeing him altogether, out of sympathy for his feelings.

4

The Cause

Etc., etc., etc.

Here is a list of things that contemporary professional healers in both conventional and alternative medicine believe cause psoriasis. It is not definitive. Other readers with psoriasis will, I am sure, be able to double its length.

Overactive T-cells (which normally help protect the body against infection, but in our case attack it)

Lack of vitamin D

An excess of histamine and the cellular adhesion protein cadherin, with these (post-histamine) hyper-permeable capillaries allowing too much 'cell food' to the area. It has been suggested that plaque-type psoriasis be reclassified as hyper-permeable capillary syndrome, or HCS. (Copied verbatim from a dermatological textbook – I have no idea what it means and I suspect from the breathlessness of the prose neither fully does its writer.)

Mental stress

Physical stress

Skin injury

Lack of sunlight

Streptococcal infection (the one clutched at by Gemma's first doctor)

Changes in the season or climate
Certain medicines, including lithium and beta-blockers
(both of which I have also known to be prescribed to
cure psoriasis)
Alcohol
Smoking
Obesity
Airborne particles
God, punishing arrogance and general sin (mainly from
southern American Christians)

Dietary causes (requires a subsection that could go on for ever):

Red wine
Tomatoes
Beef
Smoked meats
Orange juice
All teas
Pepper
Peppers
Coriander
Cumin
Nutmeg
Walnuts
Etc.
Etc.
Etc.

We seem to be the wimpiest men and women on the planet.
We can't even handle weather, let alone any tasty food. How

are we supposed to live? Sitting quietly indoors wearing a medical mask which we only remove to eat porridge.

Here is a list of things that sufferers themselves have informed me cause outbreaks:

Love lost
Love found
Money troubles
Mother, father or friend dying
Impending marriage
Marriage
Divorce
Ipswich Town Football Club being demoted from the
    Premiership
Too little sun
Too little moisturiser
The Arab/Israeli war

This is the self-portrait of the psoriatic person: sensitive to the point of touchiness. It's never right for a psoriatic. To blame both marriage and divorce, as one acquaintance of mine did, is a touch self-indulgent. But this list is testimony to the fact that when no good cause can be found, we start looking in the most bizarre places for one, rather than ask the question, does there have to be a cause for our psoriasis? This then opens up the ghastly thought that if there isn't a cause there might not be a cure, and that sends us scurrying back to look even harder for a cause.

Here is a list of things that I have at one time or another believed to be at the root of my psoriasis:

My mother
My wife
My family
My landlord
Architectural salvagers ripping out sections of a derelict
farmhouse I bought in Wales
Campers making fires in and around the above house
Central heating
Dry air
Driving (particularly on the M4 at the point my dad was
killed)
Telling lies
Writing about psoriasis (felt it sting as I typed that)
Interviews
The barber
The dentist
Smoking dope
Writer's block
Coffee
Whisky younger than ten years old

On the Wikipedia website, under 'Causes of psoriasis' the first
sentence reads, 'The cause of psoriasis is not fully understood.'
Somewhat of an understatement, I'd say. But our disease invites
understatement. Many friends with ghastly glistening, flaky
markings all over their body have told me how when they
first undressed in front of a dermatologist they got a reaction
of, 'Mmm, yes, I see, yes . . .' Rather than the more human
one of, 'Holy Moses! That is friggin' revolting!' It's as if the
truth that psoriasis is a terrible disease whose cause nobody
understands, has to be denied.

Psoriasis comes and goes either for no reason or for its own incomprehensible reason – it is our fault that we try to make sense of its arrivals and departures. The myths we create, which we call causes, tell us more about each other and the time we live in than our disease.

Psoriasis, though a disease of our exterior, turns us in on ourselves as we hunt for its source. When nothing external seems to be the cause we convince ourselves that the weakness must lie within us. We become like paranoid governments letting loose the secret police on our own citizens. And I am afraid we all too often permit torture.

Chicken and egg situation

Claire had got into a state of high anxiety about having to tell Robert about the plaques all over her buttocks. More than once she had sat him down, taken a deep breath and tried to get to the point, but she had always veered off at the last moment. One afternoon she made a detailed inspection of her skin. Her psoriasis had been steadily getting worse for years, like rising damp seeping into the foundations of a building. She was used to it, but for someone seeing it for the first time it would be shocking and repulsive. My own psoriasis had made a slow arrival whereas Gemma's had appeared overnight. I have no idea which is worse. The patterns of your own psoriasis always seem more painful than anybody else's.

Claire wasn't a coward and wasn't stupid and she realised that she had to grasp the nettle. She had set a date to tell Robert, on the next weekend she was to see him, and had told her old chum Thicket to ring her at six in the evening on the Saturday to check she had done so.

When Thicket rang, Claire whispered, 'Can't really talk, but the most amazing thing, it's gone.'

Thicket said, 'Oh well, that's all right then. Hold on, are you telling the truth?'

'Yes. It went over three days. You know what it was? Eggs. You know last week I told you the fox had dug under the wire and got the hens?'

'Yes.'

'Well, I ran out of eggs on Tuesday and by Friday afternoon my skin had started changing. Do you realise what that means?'

'You think the fox got your psoriasis too?'

'No, you idiot. I must have an allergy, isn't it incredible?'

'Well don't eat any eggs, then,' said Thicket.

'Of course I won't, what do you think I am? It's good though, isn't it? I'd show you if it wasn't on my bum.'

'I don't mind. Show me, please. Are they all pink and smooth?'

'What?'

'Your buttocks.'

'Bye-bye.'

Claire had an arrangement of three mirrors in her bathroom to inspect her back and bum. We psoriatics have all contorted ourselves trying to check out the latest skin development. She had started by backing towards a full-length mirror and looking at herself through her legs, but had graduated on to a sophisticated three-mirror set-up which preserved more of her modesty and gave a better view of her buttocks and thighs.

Hourly checks, which then became three hourly and then daily, convinced her that the patches were fading. And as soon as her skin was healthy she told everyone – Robert first – about her skin disorder. She could laugh about it now she no longer had it. A period of celebration followed. It was eggs! Twenty years! From the age of twenty-five to the age of forty-six she had suffered from debilitating psoriasis, which had crawled over her leaving drifts of dead skin behind it, and all the time it was only eggs. Eggs!

It made her hate eggs. But not her chickens, whom she forgave for producing their detested eggs. To the seasoned observer of skin disorders the fact that the source of the problem was linked to her livelihood does not seem a co-incidence. I have known many sufferers whose skin disease seemed to have the single aim of ruining their career – the film actress Sam, for instance, who used to get attacks on her chin whenever she knew close-ups were in the schedule.

Claire rebuilt the chicken run fence, digging it deeper into the ground, and restocked with her fowl – which included quail (which varied in colour from brown to grey, and often had a reddish, blue or white patterning), and the Golden Silkie, which uniquely for a chicken had five toes. She also kept a pair of Gloucester Old Spot pigs, which looked like they were straight out of a Stubbs painting, and little brown Jacob sheep which sauntered around under the apple trees in the orchard.

Claire walked amongst her little flock – no longer wearing baggy nighties as she had at the height of her sheet/clothes-rubbing paranoia – throwing the feed and singing, 'I'm getting married in the morning!' And now she didn't have to hide her flaky red bottom from Robert she could extend her sexual position repertoire with him – much to his, and her, delight.

33

In time, she really hated eggs. I once saw her pick one up and growl at it. She blamed the little things for the two decades of trouble she had been through, the difficulties with boyfriends, with love, with parties, with just functioning as a human being when half her skin was falling off. She sought eggs out everywhere and expelled them from her existence. She *didn't* join the tribe of people who interrogated waiters to find out if there was a certain ingredient in a dish – she was too polite for that – but she was vigilant.

A few months later, at a friend's daughter's wedding, she ate some egg by mistake. She was drunk and carefree and having a hell of a good time enjoying social interaction unmarred by worries about what she looked like, and didn't notice until it was too late. The egg was an ingredient of aïoli in a fish soup. Nothing happened to her skin. She went to the fancy mobile toilets parked behind the marquee and checked out her thighs in the middle of the meal. Nothing. Her skin was as clear the day she ate egg as the day before it, and it remained clear. This made her curious about eggs. She had a bite of a meringue. She was fine. Two months later she ate a greedy mouthful of sponge cake at my house (against my advice). Her skin was fine afterwards. Fine. In fact her face, which had once always been framed in a dusting of dry skin, looked better than before, perhaps because of the dawning realisation that she was no longer allergic to eggs. She had cast off the blight that crippled her life once and for all.

She got married, and Robert moved into her farmhouse near the Thames in West Gloucestershire. He was curmudgeonly and set in his ways, but they settled happily enough together. Within a year she was regularly eating omelettes, scones, custard, cakes, pies and boiled eggs at breakfast with no ill effects.

Ten months into her new married life she was hit by a heavy crash. The stuff spread across the backs of her legs, on to her buttocks, up her sides and on to her back, like mould through the leaves of a fruit tree. She immediately stopped eating eggs. But it didn't help. It didn't even slow it. She widened the ban to dairy products, and that did nothing either.

She started to walk backwards to the bathroom again, but soon realised that she couldn't go on like that.

Sitting on the sofa together watching television on Saturday night with their two spaniels on the rug at their feet, Claire said, 'You know I told you about this bloody skin disease I used to have?'

'Your egg allergy?'

'Yes, my so-called egg allergy. I'm afraid it's come back.'

'Stop eating eggs, come on. Use a bit of willpower.'

'I have – but it's still come back.'

'You're making it sound like it's something terrible.'

'It's not pleasant, Robert.' She sighed. 'I'd better show you. Look.' She stood up and unbuttoned her jeans, lowering them. There were red flaky shapes at the top of her thighs and across her bottom. Both spaniels stood up and stared at the flesh, then they settled back down again. She was scared Robert was going to be repulsed.

'Hey,' he said gently, and he took her hand. When she turned he saw there were tears in her eyes. 'Hey, hey, hey . . .'

'It's not catching,' she gulped, tugging up her jeans.

'Sit down.'

'Please don't be put off.'

'Sit down,' he patted the sofa next to him, and held her hand again. 'It's fine, I don't mind at all. If it's all right for those two' – he said indicating the dozing dogs – 'it's good enough for me! A spot of sweet itch never put me off a horse! Stop worrying about what I think. It would take a lot more than some raw patches of skin on your bum to put me off, I can tell you.'

'It gets worse than that. It goes up my back.'

'It doesn't matter,' smiled Robert. 'It doesn't matter a jot. I love you, I'm married to you, and neither of those things will ever change. Ever. No matter what.'

She threw her arms around his neck and sobbed into his shoulder. 'Oh God, I love you,' she said. 'Thank you, thank you.'

When he had brought her a stiff pink gin he said, 'Actually, I've got something you don't know about that I should have told you a long time ago, and have been too much of a coward to. Probably a good time to get it off my chest now.'

'What?' Claire said.

'A long time ago, when I was nineteen, I got a girl pregnant . . . and, well, she had the baby . . . it was a boy, but I flatly refused to acknowledge he was mine, and,' he gulped, blushing, 'I am afraid I never helped her out or gave her any money. He must be about thirty now. I have never seen him, and have always felt guilty about him.' He paused, looking into the fire. 'I've never told anyone, until you today. Always been too damned ashamed. Not my finest hour, I'm sure you'll agree. There. I've made a clean breast of it. Do you think less of me now?'

'No, not at all, but I tell you what I do think, we'd better find him. I want to meet my step-son. Do you know where his mother is?'

'God no. I know her name but that's all. I hated her for years. Do you really think it's a good idea? Surely best to let sleeping dogs lie?'

'It's not a sleeping dog, darling, it's your son.'

Robert said nothing, coughed a little and blushed again.

'Let's start by Googling her name,' Claire said.

Robert – like my own wife – seemed to be strangely un-affected by Claire's psoriasis. There were aspects he hated – the way it made Claire suddenly modest around the bedroom, and the way she spent time in the bathroom with the bathroom door closed, and the way the worry about it was written on her face. But there were aspects that he almost welcomed, the way for instance it took the pressure off him in the sex depart-ment, and in the general personal appearance department. On the few occasions Claire allowed him a glimpse, the actual marks on her back and her bottom he never found repellent in themselves – it was what they did to Claire that he hated.

Claire, now she had given up thinking she had an egg allergy, began to comb through her life again for another answer. We used to have lunch together from time to time either in London or at her place in the country, and she would always be on some fad diet or another. She started to look at combinations – eggs and alcohol, artificial fibres and red wine – and began to exclude things in pairs, but to no effect. Then she began to worry that it was marrying Robert that had brought it on. Then she thought maybe it was a combination of marrying Robert and eating red meat . . . and so on.

Her search for Robert's son was just as unsuccessful. Nothing had come up on the internet, perhaps because it had happened before much information was available online. They tried to find the hospital records to get an address for the mother, but they had been lost or destroyed, so for a while she was frustrated, but I always thought that Claire wouldn't give up either campaign. Ever. I was wrong on one count.

Gary

You have to be an incredibly strong person not to start thinking it's your own fault, eventually. Gary, an American friend, was that strong. I met Gary when I was on holiday in Negril, Jamaica. I left my wife and children playing in the shade of a seagrape tree and wandered down the beach, hoping that people would mistake my patches of psoriasis for sunburn. I noticed, emerging from a thatched beach bar, a man holding two rum cocktails who I now know to be Gary. With his feathered blond hair and an easy smile, I saw nothing unusual about him at first. His appearance and attitude were standard for 11 a.m. on a Jamaican beach, but then I saw that both his ankles were sheathed in thick scales, and the knuckles that held the Tom Collins were knobbly and silvery with psoriasis. I had never seen such an insouciant psoriatic, so introduced myself and asked him about it. Most psoriatics are happy to talk about their skin, as long as it's with a fellow sufferer. I found out that he was forty-five, owned a fantabulous home in Westwood, Los Angeles (with a guitar-shaped swimming pool), ran the most successful location catering business in California, made a lot of money and generally enjoyed life. He was married to Annette, an ex-model, and had two kids, Otis and Billy.

38

To Gary, psoriasis was simply a 'disease of the skin', not the mind or the heart.

'People talk a lot of bullshit about stress and emotional issues,' Gary told me, sipping the Collins on his tan-wagon, the pellucid sea lapping beside us, 'but for me it's a disease of the skin, forget the psycho stuff. Probably to do with the inability of the skin to produce sufficient vitamin D, which accounts for why sunlight, which creates vitamin D, is so good for us. That's it, I mean that's all there is to say about it. The rest is hokum.'

During the summer his biggest worry was keeping track of the curling brush he trained his sunny blond hair with. But then the autumn came, not so much in Los Angeles as on Gary's body, and he got his long trousers down from the high cupboard and found his pale socks (to disguise the first little flakes that fell from his shins and calves) and polo neck sweaters. In October he mournfully put away all his black clothes. He didn't want his friends to know about his psoriasis. He wasn't ashamed of it, but he was scared they wouldn't understand. That was the kind of place LA was, according to Gary.

'Psoriasis is the sort of thing some B-movie actor would think was contagious and before you knew it he'd won an Oscar and spread the word that something was wrong with me, then Annette and I would be ostracised.'

It was best nobody knew, so Gary stopped going to restaurants around November. With the scales building up on his scalp, just the thought of the black tablecloths at the Beverly Hills Hotel terrified him. With Gary it was the knuckles, elbows and knees next. By late November he eschewed social contact, and put in long hours at the office.

By February it was building up in thick silvery plaques, and at the end of March was thickening on his shins and calves, like scaly socks. He'd say to Annette, 'Annette, honey, this skin is bringing me down, I need sunshine.'

Usually around the beginning of April he left Annette and the kids in LA and flew to Jamaica for three weeks of intense sunbathing, which always left his skin clear and brown and his eyes shining with contentment.

I did notice that Gary always seemed to be in the company of a woman who obviously wasn't his wife, and one afternoon, while she wallowed in the turquoise shallows, he confessed that on his first ever trip to Jamaica he had run into the woman, who was a divorcée from Miami called Tina. He had fallen for her small hard body and cheeky manner, and the two of them had enjoyed a raucous affair, had such fun, in fact, that when he had suggested they repeat the experience the next year she had agreed. So it had become an annual event: he flew down from LA, she from Miami, and they spent three weeks sunbathing, swimming and screwing.

Gary justified his adultery to me and himself on medical grounds. Tina was what he needed to heal his skin.

I looked at him and smiled.

'It's what Annette wants,' he said to me. 'Tina's part of my cure . . .'

I loved collecting the stories of the folk with psoriasis I ran into, and filled my notebook with them. My loathing of the disease was tempered by the nasty beauty of the infinite forms it took, and the myriad shapes it bent people's lives into. It was a torturer, but there was also something of the artist about it, which I had to admire. Also, no other writer had told the tales of the skin people; I had been led into a silenced, denied community – a godsend for a writer looking for a story to tell.

Howard

One of the most intriguing causes – or attributed causes – of psoriasis I found was Howard's. I met Howard in the waiting room of the dermatology department of Wrexham Maelor Hospital, a low-built building with a carbuncular growth of Portakabins on its back. He sat wheezily on a plastic chair, his large tummy, short legs and red curly hair reminding me of some Celtic mythological being. Part troll, part leprechaun, part elf, part hobbit. I didn't know it then, but in the folds of his belly lurked a particularly heinous psoriasis called flexural. Aggravated by friction and sweat it is vulnerable to fungal infections.

Up to this point, apart from Claire and Gary, I did not know any fellow skin sufferers to talk to, and I didn't know how it was for other people. I had never, for instance, actually seen Claire's affected skin. I thought that what was on my face was definitely worse than what anybody else on earth had, because it was so visible. I must have sat beside many patients with skin disorders in the waiting rooms of the various dermatologists that I visited, but in these places eye contact was not good. Our misery was not shared. We shuffled past each other blind with shame, and I studied the carpet or curling copies of *Country Life* with rapt determination. Only later did I learn that the part of me that psoriasis made so lonely was the most easily cured – by simply making contact with other sufferers. Howard was one of the people that taught me this.

'How you diddling?' he called across the waiting room to me. 'You a flaker, then?' he asked cheerily. He was wearing hospital issue paper pyjamas and a hospital gown that barely met over his tummy.

I coughed and blushed.

'That's what we call ourselves, we who are blessed with psoriasis.' He crossed his legs bringing a shin into view that looked like rare roast beef. I had never before imagined psoriasis on this scale.

I discovered that – according to Howard – the psoriasis that dwelt in his voluminous and moist folds followed the fortunes of Ipswich Town Football Club, which was why when the Superblues had recently dropped into the relegation zone it had turned septic.

'We got knocked out of the League Cup by Bolton, the FA cup by Wrexham of all sodding teams, 2–1, and we are currently eighteenth in the League. It's not looking very jolly. All in all it's been a sodding nightmare season. Look at the state of me, look at me,' he pulled up his sleeve and showed me the crook of his elbow.

I must have looked shocked.

'You don't mind me showing you, do you? We're all in this together, eh?'

That was the first time I realised that there was a sense of community amongst some of the skin people. Up until then I had operated on my own, and avoided contact with other afflicted patients. I didn't want to be defined by my bad skin – I didn't want to be shuffled out of the normal world into the leper colony. But being with Howard eased my loneliness.

'What I want to know is, what am I gonna look like if we

get relegated next year?' He sighed. 'We went down in '85 – you should have seen me. Hopelesss I was. Then of course it was declining gates, selling players, a vicious spiral, though we did manage to hold on. It's not even that I want to support them any more!' He laughed. 'Useless sodding team. I hate them. The history of Ipswich Town Football Club is the history of an also-ran. A study in mediocrity. Well, since Bobby Robson left. Sorry, *Sir* Bobby. I have tried to stop supporting them. It's one of the main reasons I moved away from Ipswich. I was brought up in a Superblue home. Saw every home game with my dad. The entire mood of the house was affected by the result on a Saturday. It's where I picked it up, I swear it. I try not to look at the results, and not to think about who we, sorry, *they,* are playing. But it's hard to miss the football news. It's all over the papers and everybody talks about it all the time.'

I said, 'If your skin is really related to the football results—'

'It is,' he said. 'It's a cross I bear.'

'Surely now you're living up here in the North-West you've got a chance to improve it by supporting one of the regional teams that always do well.'

He looked at me with bitter disdain.

'What are you driving at?' he asked sharply.

'Well, what about Manch—'

'Don't even frigging say those obscene words.'

'Well, they do win rather a lot. They might even cure you.'

'No chance, mate. No chance! I'd rather die of sodding psoriasis than support Man sodding U.'

Some patients, like little Emily Woodward, whose Great-Aunt Carlene, Bill had discovered, suffered secretly for years behind

43

her high collars and long sleeves and skirts, seem to suffer for genetic reasons. They then despair because it seems there is nothing they can do about it – their skin is their inheritance. But, naturally, it's not that simple. Though we are always asked by dermatologists and doctors if there are other psoriasis sufferers in our families, when one in every fifty people in the world suffer, it's quite likely that it will appear twice in a large family, particularly if we go back a few generations. Most clinicians agree that one in three of us have another psoriatic in the family. It's a teasing statistic, typical of the disease, hinting at a cause but simultaneously questioning it. As far as I can see the main function of the hereditary proposition is to provide a way for doctors to explain something they don't understand but for some reason do not want to admit they don't understand.

A lot talk about stress as a cause. It's a pretty meaningless word in the context of psoriasis. For a start anyone with psoriasis is going to feel anxious and frightened, feelings that stress is a euphemism for. So it's hard to separate cause from effect. I know for a fact that stress in terms of pressure from life is not a *sine qua non* of psoriasis. Few men have led lives as blissfully free of stress as Gary, whose laid back LA lifestyle was the epitome of ease.

There are scores of plausible biological explanations, from vitamin deficiency through to over-production of amino acid, through to faulty kidneys, through to nervous system malfunction and on and on and on, deep into a multitude of arcane areas of medical science, but I never got rid of the idea that the root of my suffering grew from something in my mind. It was the behaviour of psoriasis, its unheralded arrivals, capricious intensifications, inexplicable improvements and suspicious departures, that set it apart from other ailments whose pattern was by comparison so predictable, that made me think it could be driven only by something as complex as the brain.

5

The Effect

With help from her mum, Gemma hid her psoriasis from the rest of the world. She grew a fringe to hide her fore-head and hairline, wore long sleeves and trousers and got hold of some camouflage make-up. Chrissie saw the British Association of Skin Camouflage leaflet called 'Facing The World' on the pinboard in the waiting room of the dermatolo-gist, and took down the number in case the dermatologist didn't work.

I met my local BASC representative to talk about skin camouflage in the maxillofacial clinic of the Countess of Chester Hospital in Chester. Elaine, a nurse at the unit, volun-teered for the BASC in her spare time. A jolly, round-faced lady with smooth skin, blonde straight hair cut to her shoulder and sympathetic eyes, she glowed with evangelical zeal about her work for the camouflage clinic.

'As soon as I went to a camouflage clinic I could see how much difference I could make. It really changes lives. A boy with moderate acne scarring – he was twenty-three – came and said, "I'm out of work, I feel like it goes against me." As soon as people see him they step back. It's in society,' she told me.

'Could you help him?' I asked

'I think so . . .' but she hesitated. 'Another boy with vitiligo (where hyper-pigmentation makes the skin go white in patches) on his face came in. He said, "I look as if I'm dead," so I got to work on him.'

As she spoke she took a kind of paint box with Cosmecutal written on it out of the cupboard. 'I didn't realise I was good with colour,' she said, showing it to me. 'Now I can see as soon as they walk in what colour they are. I covered his face, here, look,' she opened up a book of before and after Polaroids. The first showed a terrified young man with a pale map of Ireland on the left hand side of his face and neck. The second showed the same boy with something greasy on the left hand side of his face, doing his damnedest to smile. She tapped it. 'Titanium dioxide reflects the camera – so they still look slightly lighter in photos, which is a bit of a shame really. He wrote to me,' she continued as she leafed through the book showing me more pictures of stiff expressions and shiny legs and arms. 'He said, "I want to tell you you've changed my life." He used cover every day, and never let anyone see him without it.'

'Surely his girlfriend or wife must have?'

'No. Some patients get up two hours before the rest of the family to try to sort it out with cover. He wanted to.'

'Wow,' I said, 'really?'

'Some just use cover when they go out, it's whatever they want. It's there if they need it. There's another kind of cover that's good for dog bites and thread veins, it's new. You put it on and set it and it stays in place till you remove it with cleaning cream. But you don't leave it in place for more than four days.'

'It must be a good feeling when you really make a difference.'

'The best,' she said. 'A little girl of eight with a strawberry

48

birthmark on her upper cheek came in. Her hair was in a bob style. Very quiet all the way through. Her mum watched silently as I applied cover. It was absolutely a problem for both of them. You know?'

'I know,' I said grimly.

'When I finished I handed her a mirror and she tucked her bob behind her ears. I could tell she had been waiting years to do that. Mum and I looked at each other and just welled up.'

I sensed she was having trouble keeping her eyes dry as she remembered. Her heartfelt sympathy made me feel embarrassed, and I felt the psoriasis tighten on my face.

'We get no money from the NHS,' she said, taking us on to less emotional ground. 'All I've got are these leaflets to tell people we are here to help them.'

When I left her I stopped at the noticeboard in the hospital lobby to look for her leaflet. It was there next to 'STOP BULLYING', 'WHO'LL KEEP ME HAPPY WHEN YOU'RE GONE?', 'REGISTER FOR YOUR CANINE CARE TODAY' and 'SPIRITUAL CARE CENTRE (formerly the Chapel)'. There was a girl on the leaflet – 'The Face of BASC', Elaine had told me proudly. She was an air hostess, 'for BA', Elaine had added pointedly. She had wanted me to interview her.

'"Cosmetic camouflage has been the biggest single influence in my life. It has opened many doors allowing me to lead a completely normal and fulfilling life," the Face of the BASC said.'

It must have been these words that Chrissie clung to when she took the number down for Gemma. They booked an appointment with their local BASC member and Gemma was introduced to her correct Cosmecutal colour, which she applied to her neck and forehead where the psoriasis was clearly established. Chrissie gave her a compact to make sure everything was in place.

There was a boy called Fred who Gemma liked but had had to keep at arm's length for months. She wanted to let him get close but was scared that he'd dump her if he knew what she really looked like. They had kissed, in the safety of a dark recess in the art block during the school disco. She loved the sanctuary of darkness, and often suggested to Fred they took evening walks together. She could look at him without fear when it was dark, and let him put his hand on her face to brush away her hair. It felt glorious.

When he suggested a trip to Alton Towers she bit her lip.

'Is it open at night? It would be fun at night, wouldn't it?' she said.

'It's a day trip,' he said. 'My dad's driving us up there. Ask your mum if it's okay. It costs thirty-two pounds.'

Chrissie was pleased for her. She liked Fred.

'I don't think I can do it,' Gemma told her mum. 'The rides will sweep the hair from my face and if it rains my cover will be ruined . . .'

Chrissie sighed. 'We'll have to put it on extra-thick.'

'Oh God,' said Gemma.

Chrissie sighed. 'You don't have to go if you don't want to,' she said.

'I could fake flu,' Gemma said, 'but I won't. I have to stay strong.' She reached out for her mum's hand. 'I refuse to let this destroy me. I must be brave.'

Chrissie took her in her arms. 'Oh baby,' she said, 'you are, you are.'

She dressed in a polo neck sweater with long sleeves, a[p] cover down the left side of her face and neck, and held dow[n] her hair with both her hands when they were on the rides. It was a baking day, and everybody kept saying, 'Aren't you hot in that?'

A ride called Oblivion hurtled them into a hole in the ground and then sent them careering around a circuit until it felt like her arms were going to be torn off holding her hair down. After that Gemma and Fred broke away from his family and went to get a cup of tea. Fred queued at the counter, from where he watched Gemma taking out her compact to inspect her face.

He put the teas on the table. Gemma had hidden the compact.

'Why do you always look at yourself in the mirror? Don't you know you look beautiful?' Fred asked, sitting down.

She had got into the habit of checking the state of her make-up every time she thought she wasn't being watched. She wondered what to say. She thought about lying, looked at Fred's expression of concern and took a deep breath.

'Have you ever wondered why I always keep my hair over my eyes?'

Fred scratched the back of his neck and looked down into his tea.

'I've got this skin thing . . .' she said.

'Yes,' he said, 'I thought there was something.'

'It's rough,' she said.

'You look good enough to me,' he said, linking his fingers with hers.

That night she said to her mum, 'I shouldn't have started hiding it, I should have told people what was wrong from the start.'

ow how they're going to react.'

)day, and then in the car on the way back his

nd sister.'

ey say?'

was really strong to come out about it,' she paused. 'I'm not wearing the make-up any more, and I'm having my hair cut.'

Chrissie looked at her daughter. 'Are you sure?'

'Yes,' said Gemma. 'I feel suffocated by this make-up.'

'How do I have such a brave daughter? I can't believe it.'

'It's this stuff, psoriasis; you know, I think it's made me stronger.'

Unfortunately it doesn't have that effect on everybody. While Gemma walked round with her hair tied back and her head held high, I bent mine forwards and waved my hand in front of my face when I spoke in the hope that it would hide my nose.

I obsessively and secretly updated myself on the state of my skin. I checked my nose with a little glance in every mirror I passed; in restaurants I surreptitiously inspected my face in the cutlery. The way I looked grew to exceed in importance what I said, what I did or even who I was. I didn't notice this happen at the time – it crept up on me. A good day became a day when my skin wasn't as angry as usual; a bad day became one of those many days when I saw a red-faced, blotchy, scabby man looking back at me from whatever reflective surface I managed to find. The only way I could feel any kind of happiness was through an improvement in my skin. I searched for a mirror the way a coke addict does and used it – like a coke addict – to alter my mood. Even on the day my beautiful, lovely son was born I remember seeing myself in the plate glass of the delivery room and feeling all that happiness slide through and leave me empty.

The awesome power of psoriasis is by no means limited to the life of the afflicted person. It spreads further than that – to their partner, their family and even their friends. Bill, Emily's dad, was broken by despair. He even managed to lose his job in a fit of rage, chucking it in when he was told he'd taken too many days off to escort her to doctors' appointments. He'd focused on finding a cure for her to the exclusion of everything else in his life, and dragged Emily from doctors to healers to therapists. Her skin disorder had stopped Bill's life in its tracks. His wife Marie grew emaciated on the experience. All she could do was stand anxiously on the sidelines, now worrying as much about her husband as her daughter. What Bill had seemed to be worse than what Emily had. Even Emily worried about her dad, and prayed at night for her psoriasis not to be there in the morning so Dad wouldn't get angry again. Bill was often told that the cause of Emily's disease was probably genetic, and when he discovered that his Aunt Carlene had also had psoriasis, he lost it.

'I gave it to her,' he sobbed at Marie, 'it's my fault.' He shambled down the corridor to Emily's room and burst in. 'I'm sorry, honey,' he moaned.

Emily sat up in bed blinking at the shadow in her room. 'What?' she said.

'I'm sorry, honey, about your skin. I'm so sorry.'

'Bill,' hissed Marie, 'let her go back to sleep.'

Bill turned, 'I just want you to know, I'm sorry.'

'I know, Dad, you told me,' said Emily.

'Okay, go back to sleep.'

In the corridor Marie said, 'Where do you get off doing that?'

'If it was *your* fault,' he said to her, 'you would understand what it felt like to . . . to . . . to be responsible for crippling your own daughter.'

'She's not crippled,' Marie said quietly, 'she's not,' setting off another of Bill's demented tirades.

The Leasehold Reform, Housing and Urban Development Act

Psoriasis can even lash out at a complete stranger. My downstairs neighbour in my flat in London hardly knew me, but managed to get caught up in the saga of my face to such an extent that my psoriasis managed to lose him his house. This is how it happened.

It was 1992. London. I was living with my blotches in a second-floor flat on Pont Street, near the Scottish church in Knightsbridge.

I didn't know it then, but an insidious element of nearly all diseases of the skin is that they bring with their inflammation, dead cells and discoloration the insane but firm belief that the patient knows the cause of the affliction and therefore its cure. I tried hard to fathom what made these red spots – which sometimes ripened into silvery scabs – come and go and often thought, wrongly, that I'd cracked the code.

For instance, I got it into my head that the high ambient temperature and aridity of my apartment was causing my 'shaving rash'. But I couldn't turn down the central heating because the entire five-storey building was serviced by a single cast iron Edwardian boiler that throbbed away in the desiccated basement sending hot water gushing through things the size of sewer pipes into the basins, baths and radiators above. By the terms of the lease this monster was turned on full blast, whatever the weather, on 1st September and turned off on 1st May, whatever the weather. So even in the mildest of winters, as 1992 was in central London, the heating couldn't be reined back. The only way of cooling the rooms was to throw open the windows, and so powerful was this boiler that once I remember coming back in the snow to look up and see every single window on the front of the building open.

I managed to ease the rusted stopcocks and turn off the individual radiators around the flat, but the system was so antiquated the fat cast iron pipes that ran from room to room still got the place to the temperature of an infant's nursery. Chocolate never broke with a snap, the butter leaked oil into its dish and the skin on my face curled and died. Even the cold water was always warm, no matter how long I ran it, so I could never douse my burning face with icy water. I purchased silver Styrofoam lagging which I taped around the pipes that ran from room to room, but the lagging got as hot as the pipes and soon radiated as much heat. At night the noise of traffic through the open windows from Pont Street, which was a rat run for cars trying to avoid the Brompton Road, made sleep patchy and I lay on the hot mattress wondering how bad I was going to look in the morning.

I never waited till morning to find out – but got up then and there to lean into the bathroom mirror. I had a compulsion for self-examination. I needed either constant reassurance or constant humiliation – I have no idea which. If the skin looked good and the spots weren't as red as I feared, or didn't stand so proud of the skin, I needed to re-check to be sure I hadn't got it wrong; and if what I saw was worse than I had feared – peeling skin and, under it, glistening crimson patches – then I immediately had to monitor it to see if it was getting worse, or even, maybe, getting better, for the whole landscape of my face appeared to me, though nobody else, to be changing by the minute, no, by the second. Checking, re-checking, re-re-checking, re-re-re-checking – all the time, whatever I was doing.

An imperious Iranian exile called Dr Nader Intezam, a smooth, middle-aged man with brown lined skin, black hair, an inscrutable smile and a flash of gold at his wrists and his neck, was in charge of the building in Pont Street. He had arrived in somewhat of a hurry from the revolution in Tehran and purchased the ground floor flat and subsequently the free-hold of the building, and so it was to him that I went to ask to turn down the heating on warm winter days. The doctor, who lurked in the downstairs hall apparently overseeing the lavish remodelling of his flat into a Middle Eastern palace, but also keeping a discreet eye on us all, explained that he couldn't turn off the central heating because it was his obligation as the landlord to keep it on.

'If you can obtain the agreement of all tenants to a change in the lease,' he said to me, 'then I can see no reason why we cannot perhaps use a thermostat, to cut out the heating when the external temperature rises above say twenty-one degrees . . .'

'Or we could just turn it off at night, between ten o'clock and seven,' I suggested. 'Anything to cool the place down a bit.' I was staring at the translucent grey socks disappearing into his soft leather shoes – he was always shod as if he never went outside, and I was always staring at his feet to hide my face.

'I leave it to you,' he said, with gleaming eyes.

There were two flats above me – one a corporate apartment occupied from time to time by a silver-haired US business executive, the other by an aged widow. The executive met me at his door in a singlet and suit trousers and said, immediately, he would be happy with the change. Walking around in underwear I recognised as standard informal wear in that building. The old lady was tall, with pale loose soft skin and dyed blonde hair. She knew who I was; we had met occasionally at the lift or in the lobby.

'Hello, Lady Caldwell, and how are you?' I was a little patronising, I admit. I was on a roll: the businessman and the doctor were in the bag, the leases were going to be altered, I was going to get my skin back in order and my whole life would then fall into place. I was anticipating a pushover.

'Not too bad, considering it's winter,' the magisterial, large-bosomed lady said from beneath her face powder. Face powder! Why was I not permitted face powder?

'I was just wondering if you might agree to a change in the heating arrangements in the building,' I said.

'Ooh yes, definitely,' she said. 'But do you really think they would turn it up? I do so feel the cold, and it's nice being cosy.'

'You don't think it's too hot?' I asked.

'Goodness, no.'

'Even at night?'

'I especially like the heating on at night.'

'Me and the rest of the people in the block were wondering if we might turn it down – only when it gets hot outside.'

'Oh no, I couldn't agree to that. I like my heating high. It's one of the reasons I live here. I've spent too many years in draughty old houses.'

I played my trump card: 'You see, my face, I have a medical condition that's exacerbated by the heat.'

She played hers: 'Well I have at least two that are exacerbated by the cold. I am sorry.'

I decided to return to her when I had everybody else on side. This meant my next call was on my neighbour below, a small, charmingly fey man called Richard Stevenson-Sutherland, who though seventy seemed like a boy of about fourteen. He had lived for many years on the first floor, in the grandest flat with the highest ceilings.

'Hello! Hello! Hello!' he said enthusiastically. He had ginger hair without a strand of grey, timid, kind eyes, and a tiny hand that was offered like an old lady's – though not like Lady Caldwell's, which gave a grip like a tyre fitter's. 'Do come in, so nice to see you, dear boy.'

He was soon passing me a flute of sparkling wine. 'To you,' he said, raising his glass with a vulnerable smile.

'I wanted to talk about the heating, Richard,' I said.

'You'll have to speak up. I'm so deaf I thought you said you want to talk about the heating. Can you think of anything more dull?' he tittered, delightedly.

I knew he was deaf. When they were painting the exterior woodwork he had closed the French windows on a decorator who was at work on the balcony and the man had had to hammer on the glass for thirty minutes before Richard noticed. His memory was on the blink too – he had called the police and told them he'd caught a burglar.

We got talking, and I could see that persuading Richard to

alter anything was going to be difficult, if not impossible. He was not a man who could handle change. He had been in the building the longest – over forty-five years – and he even objected to Dr Intezam's plans to repaint the elegantly faded lobby and recarpet the threadbare stairs. 'We've never done it before. I mean, why now? He wants to make the place look like a hotel lobby – and not a very nice hotel at that.'

Dr Intezam also wanted to remove a gloomy family portrait of Richard's that hung by the front door and put in its place a colourful jungle scene of charging elephants.

'I agree, Richard, his taste is a bit dubious, but this is about the heat in the building. Would you object very much if I got your lease changed so we didn't have to have it on full-blast all the time?'

'Do you think the doctor would consider a grey carpet, rather than red?' Richard enquired, manifesting his talent for going straight to the irrelevant point.

'I want to change the leases,' I pressed on, 'so we're not wasting all this expensive oil.'

'Change the lease?' he said, looking petrified, 'it sounds very expensive. Would it involve lawyers?'

'Yes, it would,' I said.

'I do so hate lawyers,' he said, and then veered off in a more agreeable direction: 'Have you been to the theatre lately? I wish they'd put on more Terence Rattigan plays. They're awfully amusing. Are you a fan? Do say yes.'

My campaign had hit the buffers with Lady Caldwell's intransigence and Richard's inertia, but a new solution came to me in the form of the Leasehold Reform, Housing and Urban Development Act, which gave the lease-owners of flats in buildings of a certain size the right to buy their freehold and run the blocks themselves. If I could get everybody together to buy out Dr Intezam, I was sure I could then reissue new leases so that decisions concerning the running of the building were taken on a majority – not unanimous – basis, and I could therefore get the heating proposal through with Richard, the silver-haired businessman and me supporting it. It was, I now admit, a rather complex plan, but it was the simplest way I could think of to get my face – which was now looking like a redundant flyposter site – back to normality.

During the summer of 1993 I ceased writing my novel about a badass celebrity chef to concentrate on the more important task of mastering the 1993 Act. My skin came first. My new wife asked if it might be simpler just to go back to the doctor. I replied that it would not, for I had discovered that in a block like ours, with five flats, as long as three tenants grouped together they could force the land-lord through the courts to sell the freehold. The doctor, who now had gilded the plasterwork of the lobby, recarpeted the common parts with a thick crimson Wilton and placed a large brass lion's head above our door knocker to go with the big game hunting oils inside, was taking our building into a new era.

Knightsbridge was changing fast. Property values were soaring as the rich from all over the world began to see it as a safe place to set up home away from the prying eyes of their own governments. The old money like Lady Caldwell above me, and Richard below, was being rooted out and the place was reseeded with brash new cash. In the block diagonally across from me, a small oriental man had bought every flat on six floors and knocked them into a single mansion with a disco on the roof and a fleet of blacked-out Mercedes at the front door which ferried people to and from the house at suspicious hours of the day and night.

Lady Caldwell complicated matters by dying in August (carried away by a heat wave I am happy to report) and it took me by surprise when the doctor purchased her flat. But then I realised why: the battle lines were being drawn. He only had to persuade either Richard or the silver-haired businessman to vote against me, and the freehold – which was now worth a million pounds, but would cost us only a hundred thousand – would remain safely in his hands.

It was time to go and see Richard again. I knocked and shouted through the keyhole to bring him to the door, inspecting myself in the tiny rim of brass around his spyhole.

'My dear fellow, what a wonderful surprise, do come in, do, do . . .'

He turned and beckoned me with a finger over his shoulder, his head pointed up at the ceiling, reminding me in every way of Le Petit Prince.

'To you . . .' he toasted, as the bubbles fizzed up the flute of wine and we settled into the *os de mouton* library chairs in his exquisitely tasteful drawing room.

'Richard, would you like to own a part of the freehold of this building, so you don't have to worry about your lease running out?'

'You know, I have just had the doctor here talking about the same thing!'

'Really?'

'*Bien sûr.* He wanted to assure me that he would extend my lease on very favourable terms if I didn't join in trying to buy the freehold.'

'When does your lease run out?'

'I bought a fifty-three-year lease in 1940. I was twenty, it cost fifteen thousand pounds. 1995 seemed over a distant horizon then.'

'Your lease runs out in two years?'

'Yes.'

'Well it's crucial you get hold of the freehold, or the doctor will kick you out and you'll have to buy a new place. He'll sell a new lease on this place for a fortune. But if we get the freehold we can grant each other fifty-year extensions at a peppercorn rate.'

'I don't want to leave here. It's home, well, here and Beaulieu.' He had a small house on the Côte d'Azur, but managed to make it sound like a basement bedsit in King's Cross. 'But I couldn't possibly live there all the time. Life would be intolerable.'

'There is a distinct chance the doctor will evict you if your lease runs out.'

'Would a flat like this cost a lot?'

I looked around at the lofty ceilings and generous proportions of the room. About half a million pounds, I thought to myself – but said nothing.

'I can't imagine having to move. My friend Gerty has had to leave her apartment. She's now forced to endure life on the second floor in Eaton Square – *très courageux, très, très courageux* . . . Tell me, would a place like this cost much more than fifteen thousand? I suppose it's gone up quite a bit . . .' he said dreamily, looking at me with drooping eyes full of desperate hope that I would tell him that it hadn't. He was willing me to lie to him. I didn't.

I said nothing.

'I suppose it has gone up,' he said, sniffing as he refilled our glasses, 'but one can still find a bargain, no?'

'It's not easy, Richard. Have you got something you could sell?' I looked at his furniture and pictures.

'No – nothing that's worth a bean.'

'So can I count you in with the action group I'm forming?'

'Will there be lawyers?'

'Yes.'

'Oh, but they will need paying.'

'Yes, but the extra value to your lease will massively outstrip the cost. If we divide up the cost amongst us, it'll be about twenty-five thousand pounds each, but it'll double the value of our flats, much, much more so in your case. So even if you can't afford it you can sell the flat and buy somewhere else, or borrow the cash on an equity release annuity and live here as long as you want to.'

'I don't know. The doctor said he would give me a cheap extension on my lease.'

'Have you got it in writing?'

'No – he said it would be our private agreement. He said we didn't need lawyers. I told him I thought it was a good idea . . . Do you think I shouldn't have?'

I looked at the kindest and weakest eyes of any man I had ever met.

'Do you think that's foolish in the extreme?' he asked, knowing, and fearing, the answer.

'I just think it's better not to have to rely on the doctor. You've got so much to lose. Join in with me, we'll buy the freehold, hand out leases to ourselves and we'll be protected.' I didn't add: and I'll get to turn down the heating and my face will clear up.

I engaged lawyers and got the process under way. When I passed the doctor in the lobby his manner had changed.

'So – you think you are being clever, eh?' he snapped as I bustled past him with the shopping. My wife had recently had a baby girl and there was always something that needed getting. 'You think you are being Mr Business Brains? The Mr Richard Branson?'

I ignored him mostly, and pushed on with the campaign. The legal papers were soon drawn up and required signing before they were to be served on the doctor. 'Why am I doing this?' Richard asked, the pen quivering in his tiny hand. 'It's costing twenty-five thousand pounds.'

'Yes, but it's going to put two hundred thousand on the value of the flat. It's a really good deal.'

He had little idea that the origin of the freehold buyout was actually the one-centimetre-square patch of slightly raised skin a third of the way up my shiny nose.

He signed the document.

Now all I needed was the signature of the silver-haired businessman on the top floor and the campaign would be in the bag. Naturally I had corresponded with him on the matter, and had his agreement in principle. Without him, the whole operation would fail. One night, walking home, I looked up and saw a light on in his flat; I was surprised that he hadn't told me he was going to be in London because he knew I had the papers ready for him to sign.

'How is your little campaign going?' the doctor asked as I pulled my key out of the open front door. He had recently installed a video Entryphone so could watch our comings and goings from the comfort of the duchesse banquette in his pink and pale-blue drawing room, and pad out of his front door if he wanted to talk to me.

'The Leasehold Reform Act was introduced by the

Government; it's their campaign to give people control over the running of their building. It's not my campaign . . .'

'Yes, of course, but how is your campaign going? With your little lawyer and his little court order? How is it going?'

'Fine,' I said, and bundled myself into the lift.

'God I hate that man, he's so sinister,' I said to my wife, as I threw off layers of clothing now I was back in the flat.

'The doctor?'

'Yes. What did he get his doctorate for? Psychological torture? Wasn't there a chair in torture studies at Tehran University endowed by the Shah?' I spat, proving that psoriasis can happily make a racist of you.

I sat down at my desk to look for the legal papers.

'Doing some writing?' she asked.

'Not now, maybe later. This is important. The doctor's going to shit himself when he sees this. He's history. He's dog food. He'll have to go back to torturing Iranians. His property days are OVER. He is OUT of this town, and can go back to kicking towel-head ass . . .'

It doesn't make me sound a very pleasant human being, I agree, but I was fizzing with rage at the doctor, at whose metaphorical door (as opposed to the great varnished one with its ormolu knocker) my subconscious had laid the blame for my appearance, which incidentally had recently under-gone a significant deterioration. On one particularly hot morning I had woken up tangled in sheets to see tiny red scabs on my neck. I opened my pyjamas to be greeted by a chest covered in crimson spots. I had been living with the marks on my face and torso for years, but this was some-thing new.

'That bloody Iranian,' was all I could say.

All my friends were bored and I suspect faintly disgusted at my frequent, offensive rants about my landlord. My anger was overflowing – all the pain and disappointment and heartache of being disfigured by a skin disorder was now directed at him, because he was making me live in this heat. Mad, I know, but absolutely indicative of the way a skin disorder can twist reality around its little red spots.

I grabbed the papers and headed upstairs; as soon as I had the American's signature I was on my way to a healthy face. He answered his door – tanned skin, blue eyes, white hair apparently made of some synthetic material brushed into place about three years previously, never to move again.

'Oh, gee, hi, Guy. I was just gonna call you.'

'I saw you were in, I brought up the papers to sign . . .'

'Well, I'm afraid there's been a development. You see, I'm actually leaving the apartment. I'm selling up.' My face burnt at the news; it meant I'd have to talk the new owners into joining forces with us. Not impossible but potentially difficult and definitely a delay.

'Oh – right – when are you putting the place on the market? It would be worth waiting to get the freehold before you sell. It'll be worth more then.'

'Actually,' he looked a little sheepish, 'I have sold already.'

'I never saw a "For Sale" sign.'

'No – I chose to sell privately.'

'Can you give the name of the new owners?'

'Sure,' he said, taking a breath of the hot stale air, 'well – I guess you're gonna find out anyway, it's Dr Intezam.'

'The doctor!'

'Yeah – he put in a really high offer. I would have been foolish not to accept it.'

My head spun, and my face felt like it had taken an hour at gas mark 6. Under my clothes I felt every one of the little red spots flex its muscle. The doctor had outmanoeuvred me. He'd bought upstairs, so the whole freehold buyout was a lost cause. It was now three against two and he was the three.

He had his most gleaming smile ready for me when I passed him next in the lobby. 'Everything going well with your little campaign?' he asked.

If I had been in an American film I'd have rushed him, got him on the ground and pressed my thumbs into his windpipe, but I wasn't, so I went upstairs and sulked. Actually, as Vail could have told me, if I was in an American film the doctor – not I – would have had the skin disease.

I went out and bought a thermometer, because I started thinking that the doctor had deliberately turned the heating *up*.

I had to tell Richard that we had failed in our attempt to buy the freehold of our building, and invited him up for a drink to break the bad news.

'Oh,' he said, blinking a few times, 'that means I will have to throw myself on the mercy of the doctor.'

'Yes, I am afraid it does.'

'Or buy a new flat. Do you think I could get anywhere decent for fifty thousand?' he asked.

A number of matters arose from this remark. Only Richard, out of the many millions of people in the city, seemed to be unaware of the astonishing property inflation in London. Considering it was the primary subject of conversation for a good majority of these people it was incredible that Richard didn't know about it. Nor did he seem to have any idea of exactly how rare and special his apartment was.

One thing was for certain: he would have needed ten times that amount to get a place half as comfortable as the one he was then in.

'Have prices gone up awfully?' he said, searching my face for a no. The price of his flat had probably gone up in the time it had taken to ask the question. 'Would you possibly talk to the doctor about extending my lease?' Richard asked.

'I don't think I'd be the best person to do that. He doesn't like me at all . . .' I said.

'Who do you think I should get to do it?'

'Maybe a lawyer,' I said.

No – he said no lawyers. 'Oh, what am I going to do?' He picked up my daughter's soft toy that was lying on the sofa and hugged it tight. Then he leant forwards and put a tiny hand on my forearm, 'Thank goodness you're here to help me,' he said. 'You will – won't you?' I looked down at the floor, murmured something while I waited for Richard to change the subject to something less painful, which he duly did.

Unfortunately there was still the lawyer's bill to be paid. Richard was polite about it, and paid his share, but a friend of his rang me one evening and accused me of taking an old and gullible man for a ride.

I hated having to walk past the smirking doctor every day, so when my wife became pregnant with our second child it seemed like a good idea to move out, and we bought a place in Chelsea with a little garden.

'I regret enormously having to move,' I told Richard, after delaying the conversation for as long as possible. There were now only two days before the removal men turned up

He held up his hand: 'Don't go on. I can't possibly think

about that now,' he said, then added, 'Surely two children don't need more room than one? Perhaps you could rent a room in my flat. That would be very convenient. Wouldn't it?' And once again he searched my face for an answer he knew he wasn't going to get. 'You could help me deal with the dreaded doctor and my new lease. He still hasn't granted it to me . . .'

After moving, I went back from time to time to Pont Street to pick up our mail – usually late at night when I could slip in without being seen. I am ashamed to say that I hoped I'd never have to see Richard again, but one evening, about a year after leaving, I was driving out of the West End and took a short cut down Pont Street to avoid the Christmas traffic around Harrods. Outside our old building there was a removal van with a knot of men, some with trolleys, standing behind the truck, and a few feet away from them, on the pavement, standing alone, was a diminutive figure, wrapped in a coat with a scarf tied tight at his neck forcing his chin up like a child. It was Richard. As my car edged forwards in the traffic I looked up at the building and on the first floor I could see the windows of his flat were denuded of their long silk curtains, and the rooms – lit with bare bulbs – empty of his pictures and furniture. The doctor had not extended Richard's lease after all. Perhaps had I not roped Richard into my attempt to force a sale of the free-hold he would have. I looked at my face in the rear-view mirror: the square centimetre of red skin that had started it all felt as though it were glowing – almost with pleasure, and certainly with power.

The Lizard

Camouflage wasn't for me, and nor was openness, so I simply withdrew from the world. I now feared the company of adults – even good friends – apart from my wife, and sought out the reassuring presence of infants and dogs, the only things I felt I could have untroubled relationships with.

I did occasionally go out – if it was at night and to an under-lit location – though I lived in fear of ultraviolet light that picked out every flake of dandruff and dry spot on my face. One place I frequented for its gloom was a club called Black's in Dean Street. At a party there I sat next to a drunken friend and chatted about people's nicknames, going through our friends one by one. A stranger sat down beside us and joined in the conversation.

'Who's that person everyone calls the Lizard?' he said.

'I don't know,' I replied, 'I've never heard of him.'

'Apparently he sheds skin everywhere,' the guy went on. 'You know, you were talking about him earlier, for God's sake,' he beamed at my friend, who was looking down at his feet slowly shaking his head from side to side.

I stood up, feeling unsteady, my head swimming, my heart thumping. The Lizard. Oh fuck. I felt something inside me slip and keep on slipping as I struggled out of the door and on to the street. The lighting in the tube train is not flat-tering at the best of times, and this was not the best of times. I looked at my reflection in the glass and despaired. Where had my face gone, where had my identity gone? Where had my life gone? I got back home, and stumbled face down on to the spare bed because I didn't want to wake my wife up. But she must have heard me crying, because I felt her arm around my shoulders as she asked me what was wrong.

For once I didn't say 'nothing', but told her what had happened, tears streaming down my damned face. I clenched my jaw and clenched my fists as I smashed them down on the mattress. 'I hate life. I hate it. I hate it, I hate it. I am never going out again. NEVER.'

6

The Cure

We moved to the country, deep in North Wales. The term for relocating in the hope that your problems won't be able to follow you to your new destination is 'doing a geographical'. For those of you planning one, it never works. But the weather in Wales is not renowned for being hot and dry, so I was hoping for the best. We had restored a neglected house and moved in with our two children, a girl and a boy.

Even though the heating system was brand new it had a troublesome fault. The first time I noticed it was in the middle of the night, when I was woken by the ticking sound of the radiators warming up, which they were not meant to be doing. On my way downstairs I heard the boiler hard at work; I looked at the programmer – there were no lights on and it seemed to indicate that the boiler should be off. I turned all the switches to off. The boiler continued to roar away, and the house continued to warm up. There was nothing I could do to stop the boiler running, so I went back to bed and planned to call the plumber first thing in the morning.

When I woke, the radiators and water were cold, so I went down and turned the programmer back on. Immediately the boiler fired up. I called the plumber and asked him to come and fix the problem. This was Trev, our local heating man who had fitted the unit. While he drank his tea and smoked a rolly, I told him what had happened. He asked me if I was sure I had set the programmer correctly. I showed him what I had done, and he admitted that the boiler was not set to come on at three in the morning.

I left him tinkering with the boiler and went back to check on him in half an hour. He was packing up his tools.

'To be honest, I don't know what made it come on. Probably just a one-off. Teething problems, if you will. I've checked it over and there's nothing wrong with it now. I've set the timer and the clock and I don't think you'll have no more problems with it.'

I forgot all about it until ten days later, when in the middle of a warm autumn afternoon I touched a radiator and found it was hot. I assumed my wife had put the heating on earlier in the day and forgotten about it, but when I got to the programmer it clearly indicated that the central heating was off.

I called the plumber. 'Trev,' I said, 'the heating has turned itself on again. It's on right now.'

'I can't come this minute,' he said, 'but soon as I've finished this job I'll come by your place on the way home and take a look at it.'

An hour later the heating turned itself off, and half an hour after that Trev turned up.

'Now,' he said, 'what seems to be the trouble?'

'It's gone off now, but it was on this afternoon, just like the other night, for no reason.'

'No one put it on manually?'

'No,' I asked.

'You got a ghost, then!' he laughed. 'What likes it warm in the place.'

He unclipped his toolbox and took out a screwdriver.

He glanced at me – I felt like he didn't absolutely believe me but was prepared to give me the benefit of the doubt. 'Let's take a look at it, shall we?'

I left him to it, putting my head round the door every ten minutes to ask if he'd found anything. The third time, he was clipping up his toolbox and pulling on his jacket. 'I've cleared all the programme and reset it again, I've known that to clear a glitch like this. And I've reset the clock – it's possible the computer in the programmer misread the clock. I've heard that can happen.'

'Maybe that was it,' I said. It sounded at least plausible.

Whatever he did, it worked. After a few days I ceased checking radiators in the middle of the day and night to see if they were warm. And I stopped listening for the noise of the boiler in the dead of night. I relaxed about the problem.

A month or two later we were returning from a break in France, during which I had of course turned off the heating, and as I put my key in the back door, I clearly heard the boiler's exhaust. We went inside – the house was warm.

I was tired from the travelling and the kids were hungry and whining.

'The bloody heating's on. How long has it been on? This is a nightmare!' I shouted. 'Think of the gas we're wasting. Look – it's off. It's been off for a week. Why is it still heating the house?'

I had a horrible sense of loss of control, and spent an hour with the fronts of the programmer and boiler off, reading the instruction manuals, getting angrier and angrier. I called Trev, got his machine and left a rude message on it.

Trev called me in the morning. 'Your ghost been at it again, eh?' he chuckled, adding, 'Look, to be honest I'm going to have to start charging for these call-outs, the defects period is finished, see, and well, I cannot personally find anything wrong with your boiler.'

He came over that afternoon. The boiler was off, behaving itself again. I sighed. Trev looked at me with more than a little scepticism, so I called in my wife to corroborate my story, but I did so too forcefully. 'Tell him it was on when we got back from holiday, go on, tell him,' my voice was going hoarse. I realised he thought she was maybe saying it to please me rather than because it was the truth. I turned to the boiler and pleaded with it: 'Go on – do it, do it, go on.' Trev coughed behind me. He thought I was mad.

The next time it happened I called a different plumber. I needed a technical expert, not a plodding local. Dave Kenrick of Kenrick Electrical Services arrived in a liveried van which had an entire tool shed in its back. I told him the whole history. He then tinkered away with some metering machine that Trev had never produced, and came to report to me.

'Faulty programmer,' he said. 'It happens. Who fitted it?'

'Local guy called Trev.'

'It may have been second-hand. Looks it to me. Don't worry, I've got a new one on board. Best to fit a new one and have done with it.'

Two hours later he'd got the job done. He brought through the old programmer with its dangling wires and presented it to me as if he'd shot it in the forest. 'Look, you can see here it's overheated and melted. Did you ever have a lightning strike? Well, that'll be it.'

I kept the old programmer on my desk as a hate object, which I occasionally shouted at and abused when I needed to offload some negative energy.

Then one night I got up to reassure a crying child and I found the house warm. The boiler was back on.

I am pleased to report that my psoriasis did not start synchronising itself with the boiler's malfunctions. It hadn't disappeared with the move to the Wales, but nor had it got any worse.

Dave Kenrick of Kenrick Electrical Services simply didn't believe me when I said the boiler was coming on. He came back to the house and of course the boiler wouldn't perform its little trick for him. He poked about with his meter and told me that there was nothing wrong as far as he could see and therefore nothing he could do.

'But there must be something, I mean, it's not working properly.'

'Impossible,' he said, 'absolutely impossible.' He pointed to the programmer. 'When that is off, the boiler cannot run. It's impossible for it to ignite. There's no signal. How can it?'

The problem persisted. Dave and Trev didn't return my calls. I went round feeling angry at the idea that every time we left the house the boiler switched itself on just to waste our money. For the hell of it.

In our local town there was a retired heating engineer called Jacob who still wore his overalls and flat cap even though he'd stopped working. He told me he'd given it up when he found himself on safety courses with boys of sixteen who didn't know one end of a screwdriver from the other.

'I'm too old for that,' he said, 'but if you don't go on the course and get your little certificate you can't install no more.' He was a wise, slow man, so of course I badgered him about my boiler one night in the pub.

'It's an intermittent fault,' he said.

'Yes,' I replied.

'They are the hardest to solve. They can be buggers, you know. For two reasons. One, you have to test while the problem is going on, and that can be hard, and two, when you make a change to the circuit you can't be sure if it's actually solved the problem or if the fault just isn't showing. What I suggest you do is sit in front of that boiler and record on a bit of paper when it's coming on, then let's see if we can detect a pattern.'

So I pulled a chair up in front of the boiler and sat there marking on a piece of paper when it came on and went off. It was then, while I stared for hours at the blank white casing of my Baxi 60/100, that I realised what it was that the defective boiler reminded me off – my psoriasis. And particularly my search for a cure.

Psoriasis is an intermittent problem. And intermittent problems, as Jacob attested, are buggers. I had believed once or twice that I was cured, as Claire had when she stopped eating eggs, only to find that it had returned, and I wasn't. There were also certain similarities between my encounters with the plumbers and my meetings with doctors. For instance, the dry red patches on either side of my nose and around my mouth had an incredibly annoying habit of turning healthy when I showed them to a dermatologist. Sometimes they seemed to start clearing up the moment I booked the appointment. On one occasion I decided to pretend to book an appointment with top Harley Street dermatologist Dr Le Tellier to see if I couldn't fool the psoriasis into clearing. I spoke loudly to the speaking clock.

'Yes, I would like to come and see Dr Le Tellier as soon as possible about my psoriasis. Yes. Tuesday at 10 a.m. would be perfect. Yes. I look forward to seeing you then. No! I will *definitely not* cancel this appointment at 10 a.m. on Tuesday. Thank you. See you then. Bye!'

My wife came in. 'Who were you talking to then, some kind of imbecile?'

'My psoriasis,' I said quietly, I hoped out of earshot.

The psoriasis was not fooled, and on Tuesday at 10 a.m. it was flowering vividly across my nose.

I often felt that the doctor – like the heating engineer – wasn't quite up to the task, and the solution lay in finding the right person. I went from the friendly GP to the wizard-like skin specialist and on to the wise old healer in my search for an answer. I also felt the same despair, as if the psoriasis – like the Baxi 60/100 – was doing it to me personally, as if it had a grudge against me rather than was just doing its job amongst the two per cent of the population who suffered from psoriasis. And I felt always a rising sense of losing control as nothing I did either mended my boiler or cured my face.

Screens please, nurse

The eighty-sixth Annual Meeting of the British Association of Dermatologists (BAD, yes, really, that IS its acronym, est. 1920), from 4th to 7th June, 2006, was held at the Manchester International Convention Centre, the venue that was later that year to host the Labour Party Conference. It is a get-together, principally funded by the pharmaceutical companies, where the latest therapies and treatments for a multitude of skin disorders are debated and assessed. On its final day, in the Pullman Room, there was a satellite symposium sponsored by Schering-Plough – a drug company – called 'The Psoriasis Challenge'.

This was described in the programme as 'Your chance to challenge an esteemed panel of psoriasis experts, hosted by John Humphrys (Radio 4 *Today* programme and TV presenter).'

My attempts to gain access were thwarted by BAD officials, who told me that without official accreditation I was not allowed in. I asked to register, but was informed that without the support of a sponsoring drug company it wasn't possible. There were about four employees of BAD at the reception desk, whom I thanked, and then I left, wandering around the corner to the Pullman Room to gatecrash the event. Unfortunately security nabbed me on the way in and asked me for my pass.

'Sorry,' I said, 'I left it at the hotel,' continuing towards the double doors, behind which the esteemed panel had started debating.

'No entry, sir,' snapped a man with an earpiece and a crew crop, body checking me.

'Look, I have psoriasis,' I said, pulling up my shirt, and lunging at the door, which I opened enough to see the esteemed panel and a dark auditorium of dermatologists. A couple of people in business suits with briefcases swerved around me as they went in. I was grabbed by my arm and pulled out of the Pullman Room. Half a minute later I was escorted back to the BAD reception desk, and half a minute after that I was escorted to the door.

I did manage to get the names of the 'esteemed panel', and a week later emailed Professor Markham (he, like all the other professionals in this text, have had their names changed for legal reasons) to request an interview. I told him I wanted to ask him some questions about dermatology for a book. He replied within twenty-four hours:

80

Dear Mr Kennaway,

I would be delighted to talk with you about my research. Please would you get in touch with my PA, Jane Brereton? She will be able to coordinate our schedules. I would prefer to meet here in my office if that's not too inconvenient for you.

Best wishes,
Professor Markham

I emailed his PA and heard back three days later:

Dear Mr Kennaway

Thank you for your email. Professor Markham will be at the Annual Meeting of American Dermatology next week, Thursday and Friday. Please can you give me a call to arrange a convenient time for the meeting. I have tried to reach you at home but you are in London. I look forward to hearing from you.

Best wishes,
Jane

When I spoke to Jane, I mentioned that I both suffered from and wanted to discuss psoriasis. Even though I called five times and proposed three different dates, the professor could not see me. She said it was just because he was too busy. He was in America and then Australia. I continued to call and left four more messages, none of which were returned. I wondered if it was because I had mentioned the word psoriasis to her, and worse, had said that I suffered from it. I imagined the professor and his PA raising their eyes to heaven and saying, 'Oh my God, not another loony. Do you remember that madman who tried to disrupt the panel discussion with John Humphrys? God, that was embarrassing. What is it with psoriatics?'

I decided to give up on the professor and try a different dermatologist, a man called Dr Stephen Lee, a friend of my sister Emma, a lover of painting and apparently a kind and approachable man. I knew that he was a veteran in the war against psoriasis, having served thirty-eight years as a derma- tologist in the NHS. I did not tell him that I wanted to talk about psoriasis.

Dr Lee said he would be 'delighted' to talk to me, but it still took six phone calls and three cancellations before I turned up one evening at the Lister Hospital in London to see him. I wondered if the reason dermatologists are so busy is that their patients are never cured but never die.

The crowded, low-ceilinged waiting room was overseen by a pair of harassed receptionists. You could tell it was a private hospital because one of their jobs was to bring people tea. I counted four trays teetering with dirty cups and saucers. Consultants in suits swept past us on their way to the consulting rooms after putting in their day's work in the NHS.

Dr Lee was about sixty with curly grey hair, a good smile and large yellow-rimmed glasses that made him look as though he worked in the media. He shook my hand, sat me down opposite him and started to work his way through a sheaf of letters that needed signing.

'What can I help you with?' he asked, after exchanging pleasantries.

'How much time have we got?' I asked.

'About half a minute,' he smiled.

'Tell me about psoriasis,' I said.

He stopped signing, and looked up grimly. 'Ah, the leprosy of the Greeks,' he said. 'That's what it is called in *De Morbis Cutanem* the first time it was written up in 1712 by Daniel Thaner. He called it rebellious.'

'Sounds like psoriasis,' I said. 'I have met many people with psoriasis,' I continued, 'and I know how it is for them. Tell me – how is it for you, as a doctor?'

He smiled. 'Good question,' he said, sitting back in his leather chair. 'Look, most skin diseases are easy,' he stated, 'in fact, any other skin disease I know I can cure, but psoriasis . . . well . . . it's different.'

'Yes,' I said, 'why?'

'Because it's rebellious. I think we dermatologists communicate to our patients our frustration at our inability to deal with it the way we can deal with other problems.'

We were interrupted by a dapper man in an expensive pinstriped suit and shiny black shoes, who came in to talk to Lee.

Lee introduced us, and I said I was writing about psoriasis. The man, a surgeon, said, 'Oh, that. Why don't you write about the plight of junior doctors – that's a story that needs to be written.'

'Nobody wants to talk about psoriasis,' I laughed.

'It's the Cinderella of diseases,' Lee agreed, 'it is often overlooked.'

We finished our conversation. He said that there were new drugs – biologics – in the pipeline that looked hopeful, but admitted that there had been many hopeful drugs in the past that had failed to deliver the goods.

'What about a cure?' I said as I left.

The doctor raised his eyebrows and went back to signing his letters.

It's rare to hear the word cure connected to psoriasis, and always indicates either someone who is newly stricken by the disease, or someone as slow to wise up to its realities as me.

There are three graduating levels of conventional medical treatment for psoriasis, each more powerful than the one before. The first is topical, involving ointment which is applied to the skin. The second is ultraviolet light therapy, and the third is systemic, which involves pills or injections. One bleak fact is that psoriasis grows resistant to all treatments. As one starts to yield fewer returns, we are moved on to the next.

It might seem logical to go straight to the third most powerful stage and deliver a knockout punch, but the systemic treatments are dangerous and more likely to deliver the knockout punch to the patient than the psoriasis. Of the few people who actually die of psoriasis the vast majority are poisoned by the drugs which were meant to cure them.

There are three main types of cream. The first is corticosteroids – which was what was in the little tube that I kept about me for years but now I don't bother with because my psoriasis is resistant. Then there's coal tar, and vitamin D.

Howard could still make his corticosteroids work after more than ten years, but it took skill.

'My ointment can't quite stop the skin peeling off my face,' he told me, once again in the waiting room at the dermatology department in Wrexham, where he always yelled, 'Man! How you diddling!' when he saw me sneaking in with my head bowed. 'But it can slow it down if you put it on carefully. Judiciously,' he continued, smiling. 'I'll give you a fer-instance.

84

Say I make a date to see a woman on Saturday, I pick at all the dead skin on my face on Wednesday, then pile on loads of cortisone, which lets the new layer grow in looking pretty healthy. Thursday and Friday it settles in. By Saturday it's at its best, but aging so fast I've only got twenty-four hours to use it – if you see what I mean,' he raised an eyebrow. 'So. I see the lady, and all going well, get a shag and leave her on Sunday afternoon with a smile on her face, just as the skin is beginning to die. It's a question of timing. I know I can get my face looking okay for twenty-four hours every eight days. But it means I have to have reliable girlfriends, and they can't be women who want to drop by unannounced. That would spell disaster.'

Corticosteroids are renowned – like all conventional treatments for psoriasis – for their nasty side effects. Here is a list I have collected from printed information distributed with the ointments:

Abdominal or stomach pain or burning (continuing)
Acne
Blindness
Bloody or black, tarry stools
Burning
Changes in vision
Confusion
Darkening or lightening of skin colour
Decreased or blurred vision
Dizziness or lightheadedness
Excitement
Eye pain
False sense of wellbeing – IF ONLY!

Filling or rounding out of the face

Flushing of face or cheeks

Frequent urination

Hallucinations

Headache

Hiccups

Increased appetite; indigestion; loss of appetite (for triam-
    cinolone only)

Increased joint pain

Increased sweating

Increased thirst

Irregular heartbeat

Menstrual problems

Mental depression

Mistaken feelings of self-importance or being mistreated

Mood swings (sudden and wide)

Muscle cramps or pain

Muscle weakness

Nausea

Nervousness or restlessness

Nosebleeds

Numbness

Pain or tingling in arms, back, hips, legs, ribs or shoulders

Pitting, scarring or depression of skin

Reddish purple lines on arms, face, groin, legs or trunk

Redness of eyes

Sensation of spinning

Sensitivity of eyes to light

Skin rash or hives

Stunting of growth (in children)

Swelling of feet or lower legs

Swelling or other sign of allergy or infection
Tearing of eyes
Thin shiny skin
Trouble in sleeping
Unusual bruising
Unusual increase in hair growth
Unusual tiredness or weakness
Vomiting
Weight gain (rapid)
Wounds that will not heal

There could be 'certain death' on the list and it wouldn't put off anyone I know from using corticosteroids. Because they work – well, for a while.

'Coal tar has been used to treat psoriasis for many years. It is not clear how it works. It may reduce the turnover of the skin cells. It seems to reduce inflammation and have anti-scaling properties.' This is a quote from a website promoting coal tar. It doesn't fill one with confidence. 'It *may* reduce', 'It *seems* to reduce', etc. Its claims are hardly impressive.

My own view of coal tar is that it is simply another weapon we put into the hands of our skin disorder. What kind of cure can it be that involves spreading foul smelling, stinging brown goo all over ourselves? Its pervasive stink and excremental colour stained my clothes, my fingers and my bed-sheets, and made me feel a lot worse than having psoriasis ever did – which is quite an achievement. If it actually worked I might admit the sacrifice was worth it – but as with *all* conventional medical treatments for psoriasis, it ceases to work once we stop using it. It did nothing for me but slightly soften the scales.

If we make the supposition that psoriasis has a purpose, and that this purpose is to make us feel unattractive, then using coal tar helps it, not hinders it. There are modern coal tar formulae that are a little less unpleasant, but they still sting, they still smell toxic, and they are, to me, more of a punishment than a treatment.

Vitamin D creams are relatively new, arriving on the battlefield in the 1980s. They are predicated on the unproven thesis that our psoriasis is the consequence of low vitamin D production and retention. I have never used it, but Gary always has a tube in his man bag. The problem is that it's hard to avoid putting it on the healthy skin around plaques, and it has a bleaching effect on normal skin because melanin production, which makes you go brown, is suppressed by high levels of Vitamin D. So Gary often comes back from Jamaica with satin-smooth skin, but with white lines marking the areas of the old psoriasis, like chalk outlines around corpses in cop movies.

Dithranol is a cream made to resemble a drug called anthralin which was found in Goa powder from the bark of the South American araroba tree. I liked this when I first heard it – it made me think that maybe at last somebody had stumbled across some ancient natural herbal remedy that would be soothing and effective in equal measure, as opposed to the usual artificial poisonous chemical compounds which always sounded like they were cooked up by a guy with Coke-bottle glasses in an unmarked underground lab.

I witnessed Howard undergoing a course of dithranol and light therapy at the dermatology unit of Wrexham Maelor, when I was there solely for the light therapy. The application of anthralin in conjunction with UV light is called the Ingram method. When light therapy is combined with coal tar it's

88

called the Goeckermann technique. Both are quite common. And both are reasonably effective. Ingram is the therapy depicted in *The Singing Detective* – that glorious exception to Vail Reese's proposition that we never see skin disease on sympathetic characters on TV.

Howard had at that juncture (and at many other junctures) emerged from the kind of disastrous one-sided love affair that he seemed to specialise in. And, to make things much worse, the Tractor Boys – as he referred to Ipswich Town Football Club – had, in 1995, turned in the following results:

28th January	Blackburn Rovers 4	Ipswich Town 1
4th February	Ipswich Town 0	Crystal Palace 2
22nd February	Manchester City 2	Ipswich Town 0
25th February	Ipswich Town 1	Southampton 2
28th February	Ipswich Town 0	Newcastle United 2
4th March	Ipswich Town 0	Manchester United 9
		(yes, nine)

'That's zero points off six games culminating in an illustrious 9–0 thrashing by the spawn of the devil themselves,' he said, shaking his head and sending a light fall of dandruff on to the hospital lino.

Relegation beckoned. Psoriasis blossomed. During the miserable closing weeks of the 94/95 season, Howard developed his own form of treatment for his skin. It was a two-pronged strategy, the first prong being never to remove his T-shirt or jersey, day or night, the second prong to get three times daily what is technically known as arseholed on beer. One of the functions of healthy skin is to regulate temperature and water retention in the body. With psoriasis as bad as Howard's, these

functions went haywire, and there was a high risk of dehy-
dration, leading in extreme cases to coma, particularly if alcohol
was involved. And alcohol *was* involved. In a big way. On 12th
April, 1995, Howard collapsed in the Bull Inn and an ambu-
lance was called.

He had been revived in the A & E department of Wrexham
Maelor where they removed his clothes. What they found was
as much a surprise to Howard as it was to the doctor. In zebra
stripes across his belly, under his arms, in the folds of his neck
and the moist recesses of Howard's crotch, the skin glistened
red as it generated cells round the clock that Howard's body
did *not* need.

'How you diddling? Here for your torture?' he smiled.

'I'm here for UVA,' I said.

'First time?'

'Yes.'

'It's not too bad.'

I was directed into a room where I changed into a gown,
and then sat watching an Aussie nurse in plastic gloves spread
a yellow goo over the monstrous raw stripes around Howard's
midriff and thighs. It looked as though he'd been inexpertly
and hurriedly peeled.

'You not partaking of this delight?' he asked me.

'No,' the nurse replied. 'He's just on the lights.'

'So you'll miss out on the joys of anthralin,' Howard smiled.
'Lovely stuff, anthralin.'

I could smell it: a cross between Brasso and death, caustic,
sickening, stomach-heaving. Howard maintained his ironic
smile, grimacing from time to time when the nurse touched
a sensitive spot.

When he was painted we were led across a yard that smelt

of low-grade catering to the cardboard door of a flimsy flat-roofed building. Inside, against the whirr of a fan heater, the nurse gave me instructions. I was to wear sun goggles, take off my gown and stand naked in a booth lined with strip lights. I stood there shivering while the cold lights flashed on for twenty seconds. Howard had a little longer.

'Am I cured now?' he asked when he emerged from his light box.

He caught a glimpse of me before I put on my gown.

'You don't look too bad,' he said.

This was intensely embarrassing. It was the first time I had ever fully shown my psoriasis to a fellow sufferer, and I had to admit that this disease which had mucked around with my life and my mind wasn't nearly as bad as it might have been. Howard was much worse than me.

'No,' I said, 'it can get worse, but it's not as bad as yours.'

'Fifty per cent body coverage,' he said, 'and rising.' He chuckled. 'What the bloody hell am I going to do with more of this shit, eh? Turn into spaghetti sauce.'

The process was repeated, the exposure increasing every day until I was getting about two minutes of light. Within eight sessions my face and arm were pretty much clear, though I had a rather odd reddish suntan. Howard was practically free of the stuff by the end of the month, with twice-daily treatments. The problem was that as soon as we stopped the treatment the psoriasis began to creep back and recapture our bodies. But Howard wasn't thinking about that when he left the hospital.

'I feel bloody marvellous,' he said as he hugged me. 'Let's just hope it stays this good. That would be nice. Now, I have a very important lady to see, if you don't mind, so I shall bid you *au revoir*.' The absence of psoriasis and a month and half

off the booze had put a spring in his step as he headed purpose-
fully towards the bus and waved me goodbye.

I missed our weekly meetings, so about six months after I
last saw him in the dermatology department I gave him a ring
to see what was going on.

He was back in hospital. I went to visit him.

'How you diddling,' I said as I came on to the ward.

'It's back with a sodding vengeance, my friend. I don't know
if it's the Tractor Boys or this woman who's giving me the
runaround, but something's doing it. You want a look? Screens
please, nurse.'

He drew the curtains, beckoned me inside and said, 'Take
a decko at this.'

I looked and said, 'Oww, ow, bloody hell. That's nasty. '

'Sodding infected, that's what it is.'

He was put on psoralen in conjunction with the UVA,
called PUVA. Up until then all his treatments had been external,
but now he had graduated to the systemic rung of the treatment ladder, and they were manipulating the chemistry of his
entire body. Patients undergoing systemic treatment are required
to have regular blood and liver function tests because of the
toxicity of psoralen. This medication makes the skin hyper-
sensitive to light, as well as doing a few other things which
come under the heading 'undesirable side effects', including
sunburn, nausea and vomiting, itching, abnormal hair growth
and hyper-pigmentation. It can also increase the risk of skin
cancer. To avoid sunburn and reduce the risk of skin cancer,
Howard had to apply sunscreen and avoid direct sunlight for
forty-eight hours after each treatment. He was also given
hospital issue sunglasses to wear for twenty-four hours after
each treatment to avoid eye damage, particularly cataracts, but

Howard took one look at them and refused to touch them on grounds of style. 'Rather go blind,' he said.

Psoralen is more commonly used in the treatment of vitiligo, the disease that bleaches patches of skin, which apart from the primary symptom has a lot in common with psoriasis. It is hoped that by sensitising the bleached patches they can be persuaded to go brown in the sunlight.

The psoralen didn't do much for Howard. They got the infection under control with antibiotics – though they had to use three different types, which was scary enough – and a month and a half of light treatment definitely had a beneficial effect on the tubby man, but it didn't completely clear the scabs and plaques on his body. We all knew – Howard, me, the doctor, the Aussie nurse – that it wasn't going to be long before he was back at the Wrexham Maelor Hospital dermatology department.

Howard rang me about six weeks later. He wanted me to meet a woman who he informed me was 'one of the most exquisite chicks in the world' and 'the love of my life'. I went to the appointed place, a waterside pub in a village outside Wrexham, and waited for two hours with Howard for her to turn up. Howard was wearing a stained white suit, to hide stray flakes of skin, I assumed. The woman turned out to be Egyptian, called Iman. She was certainly striking, with a long aquiline nose, thin neck and an elegant haughty manner. She had known Howard for a good few years; they had met in Berlin, where he had stayed in her apartment to try and scare off a racist bully who had been making her life hell.

'Broke four of the man's digits, didn't I, Iman? Proudest day of my life, little runt.'

Iman didn't seem the least bit interested in Howard. She

flirted with me for about ten minutes, discovered I wasn't to her taste, and moved over to a table of hill-walking strangers, one of whom she clearly fancied. An hour later Howard and I sat wordlessly as she perched on the man's knee ignoring us.

'She's always like this,' Howard said, 'bless her soul. You see, people just love her, and though I say it myself I love her to bits too. I'd do anything for her, anything.'

It got more embarrassing because she was meant to be staying at Howard's house – it turned out he had paid for her ticket to come over and stay with him for three days – but she left the pub with the ramblers and was last seen squeezing into their car.

'Call me later,' shouted Howard, 'have a good one!' But she wasn't listening. I didn't know what to say.

'I'd better get on my way too,' I finally settled for. 'Keep in touch, eh? Thanks for the drink.'

'We'll link up, dude,' he called.

Three months later he went back into hospital. It was decided to step up the treatment. The two most powerful drugs used to control psoriasis are methotrexate and cyclosporin. Both were developed to combat cancer but methotrexate is now considered too dangerous and ineffective to use against cancer. At its most basic, methotrexate stops human cells multiplying but it seems to do more than that. It only became a psoriasis drug when the skin of an American cancer patient in the 1970s who also had psoriasis (poor bastard) magically cleared while he was being prescribed methotrexate. There is some evidence that it works, for a while, but how it does nobody really understands and most are too scared even to think about. To put it in perspective – methotrexate's other principal use is to trigger abortions. The list of harmful side effects comes in a twenty-two-page booklet, and includes alopecia, infertility and anorexia, though Howard was probably safe from that.

He received the painful injections of a viscous yellow liquid every two days. I went to check him out in hospital, where he lay with his clean pyjamas on, his hair brushed and a chair by his bed because he thought Iman might come by.

His skin did improve, but the light that had always glowed in his eyes – however bad his psoriasis – seemed to dim.

'It's pretty good this stuff,' he told me, 'look.'

He lifted his shirt and I had to admit that his skin looked better than I had seen it for months, since the end of his first PUVA treatment.

But when I went back to the hospital at the end of the week his bed was empty. He hadn't checked out, he was in intensive care.

'What happened?' I asked a nurse.

'Liver failure.'

I was directed to another, smaller ward, where Howard lay in a bed with a tube that came out from under the blanket into a bag of reddish-brown liquid.

'Have any of his family come to see him?' I asked.

'No,' the nurse said, 'you're the first.'

'He'll be okay?' I asked.

'I should think so. It's just the side effect of his treatment. Now we've stopped the methotrexate he should recover. They usually do.'

'Usually?' I queried. But the guy was gone.

The methotrexate – or the psoriasis – had had the last word. The staff nursed Howard back to health but the scabs and lesions reappeared all over his body, this time in places like his shoulders and the undersides of his feet, where he'd never had them before.

'I'm sorry, mate,' I told him, when he was able to converse again.

He sat up in bed. 'Did Iman come and see me when I was out?' he asked.

I so wanted to tell him yes. 'I don't know,' I said, 'I didn't see her, I'm afraid.'

'Oh – she must have been busy,' he said, lying back. 'She'll come.'

When the dermatologist came round Howard said, 'So – what next, Doc?'

The doctor knitted his brow. 'I'm afraid it's not that simple. You see, we've rather come to the end of the road, young man. You've had everything. Only cyclosporine is untried and we can't prescribe that to you after the trouble with your liver. I'm sorry.'

Howard rang me. I took the call after checking my reflection in the silver trim of the phone.

'I've done it all, man. I've run the gamut, mate. I. AM. FUCKED. It's official. There's nothing more they can do for me. You have to laugh though, don't you?'

The Face of Psoriasis

The search goes on for a drug cure. If you read old medical textbooks there is always a section on startling new discoveries in the treatment of psoriasis, as if the cure is just round the corner, which are then never mentioned in any subsequent books. Propylthiouracil and fluorouracil, thought in the mid-1990s to be breakthrough drugs, are just two more silver bullets that failed to go the distance.

The picture for the future is not bright. Psoriasis research funding in the US – where the bulk of the world's psoriasis research takes place – was actually cut in 2005 and 2006. In 2006 Psoriasis Cure Now employed a lobbyist for the first time to press our case on Capitol Hill. He's a guy called Paranzino who has psoriasis himself. Even now I can see him being carefully avoided by the congressmen and senators. Nobody wants to be photographed with lame ducks like us. He is unable to persuade any celebrities to endorse our campaign; after all, which Hollywood star really wants to be known as 'THE FACE OF PSORIASIS'? Right. To make matters worse, nobody ever dies of psoriasis – it's so untragic, just depressing. If only Rock Hudson had died of psoriasis – then our story would be very different.

High hopes engendered by the Genome Project have now faded. Many of us were certain it was going to turn up a psoriasis gene. It turns out – surprise, surprise – that psoriasis is not caused by a single gene but by many, so gene therapy is unlikely ever to be effective. The new buzz drugs are called biologics. They are created by genetic manipulation, made by a living system and are injected 'live' into the patient. Some are at the time of writing undergoing testing by the Food and Drug Administration in the US.

There's an interesting phenomenon around testing psoriasis drugs. The standard pharmaceutical procedure is to use double-blind tests, in which neither the patient nor the testers know if the drug being administered is a placebo or the real thing. In most double-blind tests for drugs not related to psoriasis, the placebo group report little or no change to their outcome. In more than a few trials involving patients with psoriasis it has turned out that the placebo group improved *more* than those taking the test drug.

There have been so many false dawns in drug development the pharmaceutical companies are beginning to lose interest. Some say that psoriasis is drug-proof. They spend their money elsewhere. There's even the idea that if they did find a cure it would now be unaffordable, and a drug they can't make a profit from – however effective – is absolutely useless. When the drug companies have given up on you – then you know you're on the heap.

7

Alternative Medicine

Individual results may vary

The failure of conventional medicine and the desperation of sufferers have combined to create a wide field for alternative healers, a field well fertilised by the internet. The web is a way of communicating with the outside world without showing our faces. Many normal people see it as a place to impersonate somebody else – usually younger and better looking – but for us skin people it's a place we can be ourselves, slipping out of our skins for the time we're logged on.

There is a proliferation of psoriasis message boards and community sites where flakys contact each other. Flakehq.com, one of the best ('sharing a little of ourselves everywhere we go'), features pages of jargon, poems, stories, mail, legal stuff and jokes designed if not to kill the pain then at least to numb it for a while.

Bill Woodward skimmed past the psoriasis community pages on his nightly trawls through the internet ocean. He wasn't looking for solace.

'I'm not going to wallow in self-pity. I want to do something solid to help the situation,' he told Marie, when she suggested they join an online community for Emily. 'When the going gets tough, the tough get going.'

Because Emily was only eleven, none of the systemic therapies available to Howard were permitted for use on her.

The highest rung up the conventional treatment ladder she was allowed was UVA and that had not been, in Bill's terms, successful, i.e. the medallions had faded for a few months and then returned as buttons, which slowly expanded back to the size of coins. Denied what Bill called 'the big guns' of anthralin and methotrexate, he had taken to alternative medicine to find a cure. Not a treatment. *A cure*. He wanted done with it. He wanted her back perfect, as she had been when she was born – in the days when they were all happy. And the internet – contrary to what he had heard from the doctors – gave him reason to believe that a cure was perfectly possible.

After a week on the keyboard and mouse, Bill found what he was looking for: psoriasis-tab.com.

Welcome to psoriasis-tab.com. It is our 100% guaranteed and clinically proven permanent cure for psoriasis.

Thousands of patients have been successfully cured with Psoriasis Tab over the past few years. Psoriasis Tab is a completely outstanding product and there is absolutely no alternative to its unique formula. Had the effectiveness of Psoriasis Tab not been proven beyond any doubt, it would not be possible for us to make such a bold claim.

Treatment with Psoriasis Tab is very rapid and obvious results can be noticed within two weeks of its use. In almost all cases, mild psoriasis is fully cured within three weeks of use. A slightly longer period is required for serious cases and treatment can last up to six weeks (42 days).

'Cracked it!' Bill shouted.

'Shh,' said Marie, from next door. Emily was asleep.

Big Bill came to the door, his eyes alight. 'I knew it was out there. I knew it. Friggin' doctors. What do they know?'

'What?' said Marie.

'A cure. A friggin' cure. Look.'

Marie put down her crossword and got off the sofa. In Bill's little office she stood and looked at the screen.

'Forty-two days she could be clear,' Bill said. 'Max.'

Marie read:

Psoriasis Tab is taken in an oral pill form and the normal dosage is two tablets twice a day, mornings and evenings. There are absolutely no side effects and the treatment is clinically proven to be safe and sold over the counter.

Psoriasis Tab comes for a fixed price of $139 for a six-week supply and can be ordered from our website by clicking here. We do not charge any shipping price.

Treatment with Psoriasis Tab is fully guaranteed. We are so confidant (sic) about the effectiveness of Psoriasis Tab that in the rare case you remain unsatisfied with the improvement in your condition, you may simply return the empty packaging and claim a refund of the amount you paid us. Since all payments are made via credit card directly to CCNOW (our credit card processing company), your money is completely safe. CCNOW will ensure that we honor all claims for refund. The only condition is that you have to be persistent in your treatment with Psoriasis Tab for six weeks (42 days). Skipping pills or being irregular will only delay the treatment.

Bill clicked on the order icon.

'I don't know why we didn't do this at the beginning,' he

said in a singsong voice that really annoyed Marie. It was she who had taken Emily first to the doctor. Bill had said there was nothing wrong with her for months.

'Let's just see if it works,' Marie said, 'you know how we've been disappointed before.'

'It works. It must. How can you be so negative? Don't you realise your negative vibes get through to her? That's probably why some of her treatments have failed. If you can't be positive, just shut up, okay? Anyway – look. How could they make that guarantee? It's against the law to say stuff like that unless you can back it up. Hey – let's wake Emily up and tell her.'

'Don't, Bill, don't do that.'

Marie went back to the sofa. The crossword was on her knee but she was staring at the obsessive curve of Bill's back as he hunched over the computer. She was as worried about him as Emily. Emily had now had psoriasis for two years, and over that time Bill had changed from a fun, easy-going husband into an angry, dark, brooding maniac. He said he was interested only in protecting Emily and getting her well again. And if Marie interfered he went mad, though he was constantly in a simmering rage. Their lives had seemed to disappear as Emily's psoriasis worsened. They never saw friends, they never went out – except to the hospital or the doctor – and they never went on holiday.

A bulging white plastic bottle of pills with a gold label duly arrived from the US. Bill and Marie lived in Vancouver. Bill unscrewed it, sniffed them and said, 'Weapons-grade. These'll do it.' He put himself in charge of dispensing them, using a chart he stuck up in the kitchen, and photographing Emily every day in the chilly utility room, naked except for her underpants.

As he was putting the camera away one day Marie said, 'Are you sure that's a good thing – you know, to photograph her every day? I don't think she likes it.'

'It's the only way of proving it works,' he said, adding quietly, 'or not.'

'Why not give her the bottle and let her get on with it? She's twelve now.'

'Because she might make a mistake. I am doing it for her.' Bill said. 'Because *I* love her.'

Firing blanks

I, like everyone else, launched myself into a search for alternative therapies. I first saw Chinese herbs as treatment for psoriasis bubbling away on the stove in the background of Ben Elton's film *Maybe Baby*, in which there's actually a psoriasis subplot, though you feel it got squeezed out in the edit because it makes little visible appearance on Hugh Laurie's skin. You can almost hear the producer in the cutting room saying, 'Um, is this really advancing the narrative?' It's unclear from the film – which is about a couple's inability to conceive – whether the psoriasis is caused by Hugh Laurie's fear of firing blanks. I've never heard this cited as a reason for getting psoriasis but it sounds plausible, if you believe the disease is designed to gnaw away at our self-belief, confidence and even identity. It also has the cyclical element so favoured by psoriasis – I can well see how it would start cranking itself up during ovulation and the horrible wait to see if conception had or had not occurred, followed by a flowering of silver flakes when it hadn't.

I got my Chinese herbs from a woman called Mrs Wong, who also took a strand of hair and said she could cure me in my absence with it for an extra fifty pounds. She never explained what she was going to do to it. Talk to it? Shout at it? Threaten it with scissors? I stewed up a panful of the herbs, believing they might work, and forced the disgusting tea down three times a day. Didn't do a thing for me except make the house stink. Meantime Mrs Wong worked away on my hair, but that too failed to give me relief.

It was homeopathy next. Months after Mrs Wong, I went to a doctor who introduced himself as Greg with a bony hand-shake in a residential housing estate in Ruthin, a small town in North Wales. In addition to being very thin, Greg had a limp. I sat in a kid's bedroom answering odd questions about my life.

'How long was your birth, Guy?' he asked. I wanted to believe this bizarre question was the sign of an analytical and open-minded search for the overlooked causes of my psoriasis, but feared it was sheer desperation. I found myself encouraging Greg, to keep up his confidence.

When Greg said, 'I think your knee pains are definitely connected to it,' I nodded and said, 'Right, I never thought of that,' which pleased Greg hugely. What I was actually thinking was that the pain in my knee derived from banging it on the stair newel that very morning.

Greg gave me five tiny round pills in brown packets. They were psorinum, sulphur, graphites, cuprum met, and arsenica. They actually helped me. No, I cannot say that. I am too battle hardened to say that. All I can say is that in the period of time after I saw Greg, my face became noticeably less red and painful. But there the improvement ceased; I still had the stippling effect down the right hand side of my body. Greg wanted to declare it a victory and I meekly went along with him. But I couldn't be satisfied with having psoriasis a bit less, I didn't want it at all. It is a disease in which the degree of affliction is irrelevant. However much you have, it is far, far too much. How much do healthy people like it when they get a pimple on their face? And think how tiny a pimple is. People with healthy skins – what do they know, eh?

Aromatherapy and acupuncture both had the same effect on me: the practitioners' modest claims of success with their other patients immediately raised my morale. After the first couple of sessions I detected an improvement, perhaps more in my mood than on my skin, but in those days I thought maybe my skin would follow my mood. I became a convert to the discipline, and told everyone that I was never going back to Dr Coutt, because at last I had found a cure. But within a month or two I wasn't talking about it so much, and not long later I stopped going.

They did nothing for my skin, and the atmosphere of gloom created in the pokey, fan-heated consulting rooms favoured by alternative therapists, with their drooping busy Lizzies and dubious framed qualifications (often with another practitioner's name on them), intensified when I looked into my face which revealed how stubborn psoriasis actually was – in the flesh – as opposed to in our dreams. I kept on with acupuncture longer than the aromatherapy because, apart from returning to conventional medicine, I could see nothing else left to try, and couldn't face the fact that I had reached the end of the road and found myself back at its beginning.

Please klik on this box

The course of pills Bill gave Emily was tortuous. Bill stuck the photos on the wall of his den. Emily felt *she* was being tested, not the Psoriasis Tab. She stood there shivering while he craned over her skin murmuring to himself, with Marie standing in the doorway frankly appalled, but scared that if she said anything she'd make it worse. For the first week it looked like there was some tiny glimmer of hope that the flakes of skin were fewer and the red spots calmer, but in the middle of week three she got some new plaques on her neck – a place she'd never before had them.

'Jeesus,' hissed Bill.

'Sorry, Dad,' whispered Emily, 'I'm sorry.'

'It's not your fault, honey, it's not your fault,' Bill said through his teeth. 'I'm mad at the people that sold us this stuff.'

He made her finish the course. I have been advised that for legal reasons the most I can say is: 'She was no better than when she started.' Bill was a wreck. He packaged up the photographs, sent them back for his refund, and got back on the internet.

Would you like to see the real reasons behind psoriasis please klik on this box.

Your immune system in your skin is designed to protect you from cuts and bruises. If a bacteria happens to enter your skin, your immune system (the T-cells) will send a signal to other T-cells to start a ferocious attack on the foreign invaders. If the bacteria happens to cause some damage to your skin, the T-cells will also send a chemical signal (called cytokines) to your skin cells letting them know that some damage has happened and they need to regenerate and heal.

www.nativeremedies.com
Treat your skin from the inside out.
Buy now 6 months supply.

6 easy payments of 34.95 & 4.95 S&H (anywhere in the world). BUY NOW in a red lozenge.

So how does Kalawalla help psoriatic patients?

It's really very simple. Kalawalla will regulate your immune system. It will restore the T-cell balance, preventing them from sending all of the erroneous messages to your skin. Once this balance is restored, your skin will begin to grow normally again.

The really shameless sites tagged on extra cures for their wonder medicines. One I found started on psoriasis, moved on to other skin disorders and then launched into this:

If you feel that you are suffering from overweight and/or constipation from your diet, we strongly recommend that you try our product to prevent the onset of your diet becoming a trigger, specially if you have already healed your psoriasis but suffer from these two symptoms related to your diet.

Other sites used customer letters:

MMR of Washington had this to say: 'I am a believer! I had psoriasis for most of my life. I had tried many remedies, drugs and UV treatment but my psoriasis never really went away or came back after finishing the treatment. I was so glad that Kappa-G worked by taking a few pills a day and I am happily surprised that my psoriasis is not coming back!'

A seasoned skin site surfer is always on the lookout for forgeries.
For me there's something inauthentic about that final '!'
'Significant results within 1–2 months, or your money back.'
Bill always got his money back, or at least tried to. Sometimes
the firm had gone bust while Emily was taking their pills or
absorbing their ointment. Then Bill would get on the message
boards and vent his frustrations.

If you spend too much time on the internet medicine sites
their claims and counter claims melt into one.

Algi clear, natures antihistamine, children 6–12 one or
two tablets once or twice daily warning safety during
pregnancy has not been established.

Psoriasis Help with Matol Km

Dear Chris,

My son has had Psoriasis from about the age of five. He
has been to see dermatologists, had all kinds of creams
from different doctors. He is now 25. He has had Psoriasis
all over his body for the last 20 years. He started taking
Matol Kaps about five months ago and now he only has
bits of Psoriasis here and there on his body. Thank you
Matol for what you have done for my son.

Mrs Watts, November 2006

(The original of Mrs Watts' letter is reproduced to try and
combat scepticism. It's written in capitals on squint-lined paper,
like a ransom note.)

I really do not have to worry any more.

Deniplant Tea from the Medical Foundation. Licences by Mr Gheorghe Giurgiu, the president of the foundation. 'The treatment with Deniplant can be used sure, without other prepares or diet.'

www.myskincure.com

Tetrasil's unique healing power may begin to provide improvement and psoriasis relief in as fast as TWO DAYS. Also kidney for sale.

Grape root for psoriasis.

Psoriasis treatment. Over 50,000 satisfied customers. Psoriacream with exclusive Regenerativ™ peptide.

GET CLEAR SKIN TODAY

(The statements in this website have not been evaluated by the Food and Drug Administration. This product is not intended to diagnose, treat, cure or prevent any disease. Indvidual results may vary.)

New peptide discovered. Why suffer from psoriasis any more?

Grahams Natural Remedies
Australia's Natural Treatment for Psoriasis and Excezema
As seen on TV!!!

When I Googled 'alternative cures for psoriasis' 117,000 pages came up.

Names and numbers

Some of us resort to psychotherapy. I myself sat on a low cheap sofa being watched by a middle-aged woman with a long nose and light moustache while we both tried to coax out of hiding whatever it was that was causing my psoriasis.

The best psoriasis therapy story was told to me by Gary on the beach in Jamaica. He was always sceptical about any complex cause or cure for psoriasis, and clearly enjoyed telling his story to me.

'A friend of mine named David had bad p. His car upholstery was black but it looked like the Milky Way. It was a bad case. Forty per cent body coverage. He went to this random therapist in downtown LA desperate for help with his problem. So at the end of the first session he gives the therapist a cheque and makes a second appointment, because he likes him, and thinks it might be useful – he's willing to try anything. David likes the work they're doing together. I say "work", that's his word not mine. Anyway, David is a bit surprised at the kinds of things the therapist is asking about. Like, he wants to know about his mother, but only the spelling of her maiden name, and he asks about his schools but wants to keep it to names and places. Said names were really significant, and numbers too. They covered a lot of ground these two: his favourite pet, his best friend, his wife, his first car – would you believe – and his children, but always superficially. Whatever, it seemed to have a good effect on David. "It's not like that painstaking therapy that upsets you," David told me. "It's more like a quiz. In fact, one day the therapist asked me nothing but questions about my favourite numbers and my favourite combinations of numbers. It's real easy, and much better suited to psoriasis than regular therapy, all that Freudian Jungian crap. People take psoriasis too seriously; treat it with too much respect."

'Well I agreed with him there, as you can imagine. With the zeal of the newly converted, David urged anyone he knew with psoriasis to try some of this new-style therapy. The good news was that David's skin really began to improve, why I don't know, but improve it did, and he grew happier and relaxed and began to enjoy life more. The bad news was that the therapist was a con man, convicted many times. It turned out that his questions – his great new therapy – were just designed to get David's online banking passwords, you know the way they ask you your mother's maiden name and all that stuff? Well that was the information he was getting out of David, and while David was going around saying how great this therapist was for psoriasis, the therapist was looting David's bank account.'

Gary roared with laughter, his golden locks shaking around his head. 'And it worked! It made his skin better! Isn't that great?' he asked, eyes wet with tears, 'isn't that so psoriasis?'

Dr Fish

There's a place called Siva, in Turkey, where we can sit in pools and have fish nibble our dead skin. Bill had considered it many times for Emily but ruled it out on the grounds that he didn't want Emily to expose herself in public – and he didn't believe the science, which he now considered himself an expert in. He never asked Emily what she thought; he just knew it would be too painful for him, so what was the point of asking her? It was also pricey, going halfway round the world, so he concentrated on tracking down a drug cure off the internet.

Chrissie didn't care how much the trip to Turkey cost. They were well-off and if Gemma wanted to try it, it was fine. Gemma was now seventeen, and in the run-up to her A Levels was suffering badly. After she put in her two hours of home-work every night at the kitchen table, Chrissie had to sweep the dandruff around the chair, just as she had to Hoover Gemma's bathroom, bedroom and bed every day. But even when her eyes were gummed up with the stuff, Gemma kept on working. As she said to her mum, 'Well, I'm not exactly going to be out clubbing, am I, so I might as well get on with this.' She always seemed to have a reserve of strength. Chrissie never saw her daughter cry, even on the day Gemma was told by a friend that she had heard a boy say, 'She wears shorts and a T-shirt so people will feel sorry for her.'

Gemma trudged into arrivals at Ankara airport enduring a full-blown flare-up. Just putting one foot in front of the next was hard work on days like this, though she always tried her best to keep her head up and a smile on her mangled face. The Turkish immigration officer stared at her passport wondering how this fourteen-year-old angel had turned into the scabby monster standing in front of him.

On the way to the thermal bath resort Chrissie watched Gemma sleep in the taxi while the driver, called Aydin, a short bald guy, entertained them with a commentary about the region.

'Anatolia keeps its cultural treasure for many years even from the ancient times goes up to 3000 BC. Wherever you go and pay visit, you'll admire the richness of the culture of Asia Minor, Anatolia here we call the cradle of civilisations.'

Even in repose the furrows between her eyebrows, the lines around her eyes and her bitten fingernails told of the pain she was in. When she woke up the driver said, 'You are going to thermal at Siva for your psoriasis, yes? I can see. Very bad. Do not worry. You will feel very differently soon.'

Gemma smiled. 'I hope so.'

'Can I give you advice?'

'Please . . .' Gemma said.

'Very good. Listen careful. Those having a bath in this thermal for the first time cannot help shuddering with horror because they notice that the fish, such as *Cyprinion macrostomus* and *Garra rufa*, brown, grey and beige, turn around the patient and begin to clear up the spots in ill health. The familiarisation with the fish takes two to three days. These fish without teeth clear up the scars through the actions of their mouth without giving any pain or causing bleeding till the skin becomes smooth. It is necessary to get into the water three times a day and stay for two hours in each to get a best result. It is also necessary to drink a few glasses of this healthy spring water on an empty stomach from the natural source (not from the pool of course, there is a spring water source). World literature states the top hot degree for the fishes as twenty-eight Celsius degree, however these creatures are able to survive their life at thirty-seven Celsius degree. There is no other than this fish around the world with three different species. My name is Aydin. You know what Aydin mean in Turkish?'

'No.'

'Intelligent. If you have any question you can ask me. Intelligent. Any question. I will look after you while you sojourn in thermal bath at Siva.'

They stayed in a medium-sized concrete motel with a restricted view over a Mediterranean landscape of cypress, Corsican pine and thyme. The baths were reached by covered walkways to preserve people's modesty, and then divided into women's and men's baths. Gemma could choose between an open-air or a covered bath, both of which looked like regular public swimming pools but with no deep end, no kids splashing about and no chlorine. A few women sat on a shelf that ran around the edge of the pool. Others wandered around the middle and a few floated on their backs. She went gingerly towards the open-air pool but was directed by a matronly attendant with short greasy hair and a kind smile to a stream of water coming out of the bottom of a tiled tank.

'To drink three glass of water,' she was ordered, as a scratched glass was thrust into her hands.

'I suppose I'd better do as I'm told,' she said to Chrissie, who hovered behind her.

'How long does she have to go into the pool for?' Chrissie asked the attendant.

'Patient should remain eight hours a day in the pool as a two episode in a day.'

'I think that's two four-hour stints,' said Gemma. 'Right, here goes.'

There were wide steps down into the clear water, though Chrissie did notice flakes of floating skin which reminded her of the fish food they used for the goldfish at home.

'What's it like?' Chrissie asked.

'Lukewarm,' said Gemma, who wanted to get underwater fast to hide her scaly legs. 'Look,' she said trying to grab something off the water, 'a bit of me has floated away.' Then she let out a little shriek. 'Oh. My. God! Look! Mum! Eek!'

It looked like her feet were caught in a length of grey seaweed that swayed around in the current. But there was no current, and there was no seaweed either. It was a shoal of slim fish each about the length of a hand, gathering around her ankles.

'What does it feel like?'

'It's, er, er, tingling, not too bad really. Try it.'

'I'm not going in there,' laughed Chrissie. But Gemma went deeper, right up to her neck and watched in amazement as the fish swarmed around her.

When she came out four hours later she hurried back to the hotel room for an inspection. Chrissie was lying on the bed watching Turkish TV. It was just dawning on her exactly how bored she was going to get on the trip, though the next day Aydin leapt out from behind an aspidistra in the lobby and almost forced her to get into his cab for a tour.

Gemma lounged in the water with the other women, often in silence for hours because they couldn't speak English. It didn't matter. She made friends with the fishes who struck and licked at her skin. In the evening Aydin would jump them in the lobby, and walk backwards in front of them until they caved in and got into his taxi.

'I'd be pleased to offer the magical package for two beautiful women of transport and restaurant all you can eat meal to my good friends. Now please to step in my carriage and please to permit me introduce the best restaurant centre for your review.'

'All right,' they would laugh.

'What is my name Aydin meaning?' he asked.

'Intelligent!' the woman said together, making Aydin smile as he opened the car door.

'Most certainly,' he said, 'with pleasure.'

Gemma lay back in the water for hours watching the clouds pass in the sky, feeling her shoal of little friends nudging at her skin. It was barely warm enough to sunbathe, but Chrissie sat on a sunbed reading a book, quietly praying for her daughter.

Over the days, Gemma's breathing slowed, the furrows between her eyebrows smoothed, her eyes ceased wincing and the headache that had plagued her for months eased and withdrew. Her skin certainly looked better – but she didn't know if it was like just replastering and repainting a damp wall. The little fish had picked off the scabs, and the water – either from bathing in or drinking it – definitely stopped the cells reproducing so swiftly, but until she left Siva she couldn't gauge if the damp was going to reappear through the new plasterwork.

She returned to Surrey, her confidence renewed, her body less of a twitching, stinging mess, and threw herself into her A Level work. She took the exams in June, and by breakfast on 23rd August her skin was already in decline again. But she didn't care – she had just opened a letter that informed her she had 3 A Levels at Grade A.

Chrissie put her arms around her daughter and lifted her off the floor. 'You are the most amazing, amazing girl in the whole wide world,' she said in her ear. 'Just amazing.'

Which doctors?

Bill thought of himself as a pioneer on the leading edge of psoriasis research – not the projects overseen by the FDA and the big drug companies that go on for years with double-blind tests – but the unregulated stuff done by doctors who're struck off, crazy but brilliant chemists and other oddballs with minds too big for conventional medicine. It was from these kinds of guys that the breakthrough was going to come – Bill was sure of it. He felt the wind in his hair when he got on the net these days – he didn't waste time on the sites that any of us would find. He was way past them. Way past. He had looked at over 110,000 psoriasis sites.

Bill knew all about the Siva fish. There was another fish cure in Japan. What could the fish do but pick off the dead skin, basically clean you up for a month or two? He had picked up a rumour on a message board of a cure that sounded better than the Siva fishes. A guy called Dr Singh, in Geneva. That was a good sign. Switzerland was the Wild West of drug development – they could do anything there. A man called Dr Schmidt was happy to hand out a retroviral drug from his castle high in the Alps that had been withdrawn from testing after a man died on the trial in the US. Drugs that were banned even in Thailand were prescribed in clinics in Switzerland. You just had to know which doctor to ask. Bill had a folder full of names, and at the top of the list was Dr Singh, who had a cure, it was rumoured (he had not yet found Singh's own website – it was said you needed a secret password for that), which was 100 per cent effective *and permanent*, but involved something so repellent, so utterly disgusting, that the patient had to be sedated before treatment so they wouldn't know what they were going through. Apparently it was not humanly possible to tolerate the therapy, which took four hours. But one session was all you needed.

There was a lot of speculation on the message boards about what Dr Singh actually did to you during those four hours. Most people believed the patient was put in a tank and immersed in something repugnant – though precisely what was the subject of debate. Those who had actually been through the experience said they were anaesthetised in a preparation room on a trolley which they believed was then wheeled into the treatment room where the secret apparatus – whatever it was – stood. One said he thought he smelt horse manure. Someone else said that it was human shit. Bill had been on Dr Singh's trail for months and was pretty sure he knew the truth: genetically modified spiders (possibly fed on horse manure – hence the smell). Millions of them crawling all over you, eating dead skin and secreting vitamin D from glands in their thorax.

Dr Singh himself was elusive. He basically worked under-cover, out of sight of the authorities. This appealed to Bill, who believed organisations like the FDA were holding back research. Dr Singh's patients were apparently approached by the doctor rather than the other way round. It was pure chance that they got the treatment. Dr Singh lurked outside skin clinics and propositioned the patients, speaking English with a strong German accent even though he looked Indian.

Bill had told Marie about Dr Singh many times. Marie did not like the sound of putting Emily under anaesthetic for an unregulated backstreet cure.

'Can we at least know what it is?' she asked, exasperated.

'No. It's still in the development stage. He can't risk it getting out.'

'Bill . . .' sighed Marie. 'I'm not doing that. I have to know. It could be anything.'

He snapped round at her, his eyes blazing. 'WHY DO YOU WANT TO FUCK THIS UP FOR HER?' he screamed. Marie stepped back from the blast. Bill was away again. In her bedroom Emily heard the shouting and closed her eyes. 'DON'T YOU FUCKING REALISE THAT WE HAVE TO TAKE RISKS IF WE'RE GOING TO GET THE BEST NEW TECH-NOLOGY FOR HER?' Bill was going critical. 'SHE WILL

COME OUT OF THE SINGH THERAPY CLEAR FOR FUCKING EVER. DOESN'T THAT MEAN ANYTHING TO YOU? *DOESN'T IT?* I'm taking her to Switzerland to look for Singh. Period.'

'No you are not,' Marie said quietly. 'We are going on holiday, like a normal family.'

'That's a waste of money and time.'

'I am making the arrangements,' Marie said. 'This is going to stop.'

'At least put her on the calcipotriol and betamethasone dipropionate trial.' This was another of Bill's recent discoveries.

'No more drug trials. Trials – that is exactly what they are. That's what she goes through each time. A trial. So no more.'

'Combined therapy is known to be superior to monotherapy, she's never been on a combined. This trial combines calcipotriol and betamethasone dipropionate in a single vehicle to achieve optimal frigging delivery of both substances into the skin. Everybody thinks it's going to be the breakthrough we're waiting for.'

'Can't you see, Bill, you are making it worse? Can't you see that? With your photos and your charts and your crazy all-night sessions on the internet. Dragging her here and there, never letting her just forget it for a moment and try to live her life . . .'

'Forget it? No, I will not just forget it, because I am actually a good father who thinks the best thing is to do something for his child when they're ill, rather than just say something comforting like you. You see I will not give up. I will not.'

'She needs a holiday, not immersing in horse shit. It's you, you – you who are immersed in horse shit. All your stupid theories . . .'

'They are not stupid. I'm evaluating them.'

'Well so am I and they stink. Our daughter does not need to go on a drug trial. She's a nervous wreck. Our child actually shakes with nerves. She's eleven years old and she's got the shakes. She should be full of the joys of life.'

'Hel-lo! That's the psoriasis,' he said in his singsong voice.

'It's not the psoriasis. We've seen other patients with it who aren't anything like her. It's you and your tests and your creams and your pills and the pressure she feels she's under . . .'

'Oh hell,' Bill said putting his head in his hands. He sat on the arm of the sofa and started crying. 'I just want to help my baby,' he moaned, 'I just love her so much . . .'

Marie's eyes glowed for a moment. 'Well you can start by pulling yourself together. Stop snivelling. How dare *you* cry? It's her who has it, not you. This has nothing to do with you, but it's you who is cracking up. Get a grip. Act like a man, for God's sake. She needs you to be strong. I do too. Think about her for once. This is NOT about you. Geddit?'

And with that Marie turned to the door.

We get psoriasis, that's bad enough, but then they try to cure us, and that's even worse. Psoriasis led me by the nose from doctor to doctor, on a circuitous journey around the medical profession, through a maze of alternative therapies, on and off a carousel of counsellors, hypnotists, dieticians and psychiatrists, before delivering me back to the doctor I first went to. Most of us sufferers have spent years being ground down in the mill of cures. We've had our dreams of getting better destroyed again and again as each successive physician or therapist has first promised and then failed to get the stuff off our exhausted bodies and out of our desperate minds.

Nothing in the world of herbs, doctor fish, weird Swiss drugs, mineral extracts, tonics, strange diets, acupuncture, hypnotherapy, magnetic field therapy, oxygen therapy, chelation therapy, reflexology, chiropractic, physiotherapy or massage is powerful enough. We need stronger magic. These therapies are often dispensed by good, hardworking, honest practitioners, who want nothing more than to give relief, but they have little idea what they are up against. They are climbing Mount Everest in flip-flops. They are no match for psoriasis — not the most dangerous, or even the most powerful, but the smartest disease of them all. It runs rings round all of them, as it does round the conventional doctors and indeed the sufferers. This is because psoriasis is the grand master of illness, the Kasparov of disease.

I remember once leaving a herbalist holding a brown paper bag of burdock and sarsaparilla. I wasn't exactly hopeful at the time. A man from the council was removing bubble gum from the pavement with a machine called the Gumbuster which was a high-pressure hose that blasted the pink spots off the stone. I watched the spray-gun buck with the power of the water. He saw me staring and turned off the compressor, flashing me a big smile. He was an Indian-looking guy.

I felt like saying, 'If I lie down and undress, you wouldn't give me a waft with that, would you?'

8
The Silver Bullet

My Baxi 60/100 central heating boiler? I didn't call in the alternative healer plumber, though there was something of the wizard about Jacob. He worked out that the water in the system was moving by convection through the pipes, and this was spinning the pump sufficiently to generate an electrical signal which went back to the boiler and sparked it up apparently spontaneously. Jacob fitted a valve to prevent the water moving through the pump and it never happened again. He cured it.

When nobody was around – because they would have thought me insane – I pulled up a chair in front of the boiler, as I had in the past, sat on it and read a book, simply wallowing in the silence. Just before 5 p.m., when it came on to warm the chilling house, I looked at my second hand and heard the tick, *woomph* of the Baxi doing its work, then the comforting ticking of the radiators heating up. I was in bliss. It was fixed. I didn't have to worry about it any more. The confusion of not understanding was over.

My friend Mark – who unlike most people in this book has absolutely *no* psoriasis or any other skin disease – and I were out walking on the Minera mountain in North Wales. The lace was flapping on his shoe and he stopped to retie it.

'It's got a knot,' he said.

I sat on a stone, glad to rest for a moment and admire the deep green, sheep-sprinkled hills.

'I like knots,' he said.

'Why?' I asked.

'Because they are problems which have solutions. How many problems in life can you say that about?'

Very, very few. His shoelace and my Baxi boiler. Almost nothing else. Definitely not my skin.

But we skin people all long for the silver bullet. We know it's not there, it doesn't even exist, but we cannot help fantasising about finding something, a pill, a drug, an ointment, a therapy of some sort which will magically erase these crusts from our skin.

For the first half of the nineteenth century it was assumed that cholera was airborne. However, a London doctor called John Snow did not accept this 'miasma' (bad air) theory, arguing that in fact it entered the body through the mouth. He published his ideas in an essay, 'On the Mode of Communication of Cholera', in 1849. A few years later, Snow was able to prove his theory when in August 1854 a cholera outbreak occurred in Soho. After careful investigation, including plotting cases of cholera on a map, Snow was able to identify a water pump in Broad (now Broadwick) Street as the source of the disease. He had the handle of the pump removed, and cases of cholera immediately began to diminish. Where is our John Snow? Where is our pump handle?

Nowhere to be found, is the answer.

Howard rang me one Sunday evening sounding worn-out.

'I need to meet you, talk to you, something's come up. I think I've solved the problem of my skin.'

'You've found the silver bullet?'

'Yeah,' he hesitated, 'you could say that.'

We met in the pub by the river in Llangollen, a town

clustered around an old bridge nestled in hills. A fall of snow had recently thawed. Here and there, in the lees of walls and trees, small lumps of grey substance were the only sign of the snow, apart from the rushing roaring river. It was so high I could hear it from inside the pub, where Howard was looking into a pint on his own in the corner.

'How you diddling?' I said.

He sighed. I could see his scalp through his ginger hair — it was raw, like his knuckles. When he looked up I saw that he had a harsh attack on his cheeks and forehead.

'It's tough, I can see,' I said.

'I got you something at an antiques stall in the market.' He passed me an old-fashioned ink standard.

'Thanks Howard, that's kind.'

'You're a writer, it's for a writer. I thought it might inspire you, though you probably don't use ink, do you? Some high-tech keyboard no doubt.'

'Yes, but I'll put this on my desk,' I said. 'So — what's going on?'

'Terrible, terrible day yesterday. The worst. You know I sometimes do some driving for a catering firm when roofing gets slow? Well, I drove out to some sodding great big house in Shropshire yesterday for a wedding. Sir Hufton Bufton Fortescue or someone. I park up behind the marquee and start lugging in the plates and Champagne and all the crap for the banquet. On about the fifth run you'll never guess who I see at the other end of the tent — only Iman. Obviously I call out, and go over to her.

'"What are you doing here?" she asks.

'"Delivery-man for the caterers. Look, if you're going to be here I'll slip in and join the party after it gets going."

'Her face sank. That hurt – I admit it. But not as much as her reply when I asked if she was a friend of the bride or groom.

'"I am the bride," she smiled.

'All right, all right, yes yes yes, I did, I admit it, once dream of marrying the girl. Love does that to you. I knew it was a long shot but once or twice way back there in Berlin when we met and I looked after her and she was so kind to me I did dream about a future with her – but that was not why I was so sodding pissed off. I had let that dream die – like so sodding many before it. No, what hurt, really hurt, was that she hadn't even invited me to her wedding. For fuck's sake,' his voice went hoarse. 'You know?'

'Yeah, I know. She always struck me as a bit of a bitch.'

'Hearing you say that hurts me . . .' He shook his head, then took up the thread again. 'She went on about how limited the numbers were and how she didn't have my address and blah, blah until someone called her away. They wanted us to clear everything away that night so I went back to the van to wait, and sat there thinking about letting down the marquee or spiking the lobster bisque starter with acid. I reckoned I could easily have got over to Kevin's in Oswestry and back with a bag of two hundred microdots before dinner. Then I thought about letting down everyone's tyres – but what's the point, honestly? I took a nap in the cab and then guess what?'

'You dropped the wedding cake?' I asked.

He smiled ruefully. 'If only,' he said. 'I'd sodding love to have done that. No, I switched on the van radio and it was tuned to 5 Live and it was the footy results. I tried to turn it off. I knew I shouldn't be listening, but I knew we were in the play-offs for promotion. Up it came. Charlton one, Ipswich nil.'

He paused and let out another huge sigh.

'So we aren't going up . . . What a sodding life.'

After a while I said, 'The river's big tonight, you can hear it.'

'Yeah,' Howard said, 'the river god is angry tonight.'

We had a few more drinks, and then I said I'd drive him home, but he passed on the offer, said he wanted to stay till closing and walk home. He had two more beers, stood up, left the pub and trudged on to the bridge, where he leant against the stone parapet and looked down into the churning blackness below. It was calling to him – inviting him to join it, to leave the world with all its weary pain and be engulfed by oblivion once and for all. Like some huge beetle he clambered on to the old stone wall and slipped over the other side into the hurtling water.

Dr Bortot and the skin meridian probe

The highest rate for psoriatic suicides is in Australia. I learnt that from Sandra Gibbons, the guru for British alternative treatment of psoriasis.

'It's because you can't cover up so easy in a hot country,' she said.

Sandra's book *Beat Psoriasis: Simple and Effective Treatment – the Natural Way,* first published in 1980, is the biggest selling publication on the subject, and, she told me, often reprints three times in a year.

As well as being a writer, Sandra, a youthful sixty-one, runs a clinic in Fulham, West London, and it was there that I spoke to her with, I must admit, the single aim of exposing any quackery. I had just grown too cynical, and too angry with the snake-oil salesmen.

'My mother was a cosmetologist,' she told me, 'so I was brought up with the skin.' My quack antennae twitched at this promising start.

'And your specialty is psoriasis,' I said.

'Well I know I know how to clear it because I've done it myself, not cure of course. It's morally wrong to offer a cure. When HarperCollins bought Thorsons, who published *Beat Psoriasis,* they wanted to put the strap line on the cover **CURE** PSORIASIS THE NATURAL WAY. I had a hell of a fight with them over that. I wouldn't stand for it. They just kept saying it would increase sales, but I wouldn't do it. I didn't cave in.'

Disappointed by this display of integrity I moved on.

'What is your theory about psoriasis?' I asked.

'Anybody with psoriasis was born without malic acid in the liver,' she stated simply, adding, 'so they cannot break down saturated fat – that's animal fat – so the toxins are coming out of the skin. They should be coming out the normal way – as nature intended,' she delicately put it. I realised that she was saying that as a psoriatic I am basically defecating through my skin. Not pleasant, sure, but in some way plausible. I could feel myself falling under the spell of the psoriasis healers, whose promise of smooth skin put logic on hold.

'Some people say it's unexpressed thoughts or feelings coming through the skin,' I stated, joining in.

'You mean stress?' she said – using the British word for feelings. 'Stress won't cause it – it's a virus or bacteria that causes it.'

'Is there more of it about now than twenty years ago?'

'Definitely, yes.'

'Why?'

'Pollution and diet and more chemicals.'

'So how does your treatment work?'

'We, that's me and my husband Geoffrey, use a MORA therapy diagnostic tool invented by Dr Bortot in South Africa.' I was clearly back in crank land. I suppressed a smile. 'It's a brand of electric acupuncture. We attach probes to a patient linked up to the skin meridian, and get a reading which should be fifty.' She said this as if it was barely more than common sense. 'With psoriatics it reads over seventy. And nine times out of ten the hormones meridian is seventy.'

'But how does Dr Bortot's machine actually work?'

'Well,' she said, sounding like she thought I was simple, 'put almonds on the machine, it sends the reading up to seventy.' I am surprised she didn't add, 'idiot'. 'Same with tomatoes, or any red food. So I say to the patient, don't eat those tomatoes till we clear you out.'

'What's wrong with red food?'

'Red foods heats the blood, makes the body out of balance.'

'You mean they fall over?' I said, trying to keep a straight face.

She ignored that. 'A lot of detective work comes in,' she continued, 'to find the right diet. And then it takes twelve weeks for the skin to heal because it heals last. They go on a totally organic diet discovered by Dr Shaffer, a German doctor. Dietary factors differ with the digestive system, but they usually come off dairy.'

I reminded myself that I was talking to a highly respected practitioner of alternative medicine.

'What about cortisone?' I asked.

'Cortisone thins the skin and affects the adrenal glands. We see a lot of people from dermatologists and the medical profession. Well, they have a problem with psoriasis, don't they? Chinese and homeopathy are not that effective either,' she continued, putting the boot into the enemy. 'They tend to make it worse before it gets better – have to bring out of the system. Their biggest problem is they haven't got something to clear it.' Then she added for good measure, 'You know psoriasis.com is financed by the drug companies, don't you? Mmm.'

'It's so hard to know who to believe,' I said.

'Well, be sure to mention my book, won't you? And you can quote as much as you like from it.' As we said goodbye her eyes moistened. 'People who come to the clinic have so much courage to keep going, they're so sore and uncomfortable, but they keep on battling with life.'

I went to visit Claire to talk about Sandra Gibbons. Robert had a flat not far away in Fulham. It turned out Claire was a devotee of Sandra, and had three well thumbed copies of her books, so I kept off the subject. She was on a new regime involving a copper bracelet and meditation tapes she'd been sold by a Bulgarian while on holiday in Tuscany.

I asked her if they'd found Robert's son.

'No,' she said, thoughtfully, 'unfortunately not. He seems to have disappeared off the face of the earth, or rather his mother has, and without her we can't find him. Most disappointing, though I think Robert is secretly pleased . . .' she paused, 'well, maybe not, I don't know for sure . . .'

9

Incurable

I think it was sometime in 1997 that I realised no matter what I did it wasn't going to go away. It was incredible that it took me so long to wise up. But by then I had finally admitted to myself I was stuck with it. Maybe we have cured all the diseases that can be cured — polio, tuberculosis, syphilis, leprosy, all the great nineteenth-century ailments are dealt with. The ones we are left with, AIDS, cancer, arthritis, Alzheimer's, psoriasis, these we are never going to lick.

There was once an institution on Roehampton Hill in the leafy suburbs of South London called the Roehampton Hospital for Incurables. The words were picked out in wrought iron over the entrance. I used to pass it when I was at school near Guildford in the 1970s, and think every time, Can't be very nice going in there as a patient, though the sign probably made the doctors' job a whole lot easier. Now it's called the Roehampton Hospice. I, like many people, find it hard to accept that a disease is incurable. It was called being positive in my family — a mindset that was meant to affect the outcome, make things more likely to turn out well. So it was a really difficult thing for me to accept that there wasn't going to be a happy ending with my skin. And I noticed that people who I met also didn't want to accept that I was incurable.

'You've got that because you're depressed. You may even have bipolar. If you get the right antidepressants that will all go away,' I was told.

The same perky Harley Street dermatologist told me in both 1993 *and* 1997 that in five years we'll have a cure.

When I went into remission my mother said, 'Thank God it's finally gone. It always looked so, so, so . . . unattractive.'

And sometimes complete strangers gave me the benefit of their wisdom. 'My sister stopped smoking and it went away.' 'Did you every try peeing on your hands?' 'I heard you should go in the ocean with oats on.'

They just didn't want to believe it is incurable; to them it meant I'd given up. I hadn't given up, I'd just realised that instead of diverting all that energy trying to prevent it I was going to have to focus my efforts into learning to live with it. It was actually a relief to stop looking for cures or treatments.

Claire – always a source of sound advice – poured me a cup of Earl Grey in the kitchen of her Cotswold farmhouse and went off to look for a bit of paper she said she wanted to show me.

'It's here somewhere!' she called from the next room. 'Here,' she said, coming back in.

She gave me a typed page. 'I was sent this and read it to keep me toughened up,' she said. 'And for a laugh.'

This page should be studied as a 'de-sensitising experience'. What you've heard before rolls off your shoulders that much easier next time you hear it . . .

[My boyfriend to flaker-me:] Do you mind if I smell

your shampoo? I'm sick and need to throw up. That should do the trick. –Katharine O.

[Pastor to flaker-male member of congregation:] Boy, I really feel sorry for your wife. She must have a hard time in the bedroom. –Dean

[Day after someone in the office notices my bleeding arm lesion, this announcement is made:] There will be a mandatory safety meeting on the hazards of 'blood-borne pathogens'. –Guinn B.

[Just-diagnosed daughter to mom who has psoriasis:] If you knew this was inheritable, why did you have kids? –Kevin P.

[From boyfriend, one month into relationship:] Your skin doesn't bother me at all, you're beautiful! [Same boyfriend, six months into relationship:] Gawd! Isn't there something you can do about this?! –Elle

You leave crumbs at the table, even when you don't eat. –Roland

Hey, you have a chip in your hair . . . let me get that for you . . . Eww! –Rachelle

Lady, I can't let you try on these shoes. –Delane

[Strange lady on the bus says:] That's horrible! How can you go out in public? If I had *that*, I'd kill myself. –Lorrie

I put the paper down. 'Is this what it's come to?' I asked. 'We have to 'de-sensitise' ourselves?'

'We have to be tough,' said Claire.

'Thick skinned,' we said in unison, and as she laughed, a flake of skin fell out of her hair on to the checked table-cloth.

Bill and Marie's daughter Emily turned into a Goth. Teased at school – 'Yo! Cornflakes!' – her enthusiasm for the place dried, curled and fell from her, leaving a glistening hatred. She preferred to spend the days in a friend's basement smoking dope and cigarettes and the nights in places like graveyards, taking speed. Her gang of freaks, in black and white make-up and black clothes liked Emily's weird skin. Being a Goth, she got a break from the incessant pressure of her psoriasis, but inside she was cold, and scared of the world and the future. She never smiled and rarely ate. In the short cold Vancouver winter days she huddled and shivered and chain-smoked cig-arettes.

Marie joined a group of mums with disabled kids. They usually met at the house of a woman who had a daughter with Down's syndrome, on Thursday nights when the girl was taken out by her dad, who had left home. It was across Vancouver, but Marie liked to walk the four miles. She wrapped up well, left Bill on the couch watching sport and stepped out into the street, listing and rehearsing all the little things she wanted to tell the group. Diane's house was set back from the road; usually Marie could see the women in the lounge through the window, and her spirits always rose when she did. None of them had a kid with a skin disease, but that didn't matter. They knew. They knew the secret of raising an incurable child. Janet's daughter Jasmine was blind.

A shriek of welcome always went up when Marie went in. There were no formalities. After the coats were hung up and the coffee and cake served they just sat around Diane's chaotic lounge, exchanging woes, glorying in their triumphs, however small, and moaning about their husbands until nine-thirty when Diane's ex and her daughter came back, and they all left. Diane's ex was like Bill – he didn't like the group. But none of them cared. Marie never walked home without feeling better than when she had turned up.

Gemma was eighteen, had got into Edinburgh University to read English Literature, and was preparing for her gap year. Some of her friends invited her on trips to India and Thailand but in the end she never went. Her feet seemed too heavy to leave home, and Chrissie and her dad were not forcing her out of the door. She travelled extensively on her computer and had got into the habit of frequenting chat rooms – not necessarily romantic ones – to experience the world.

'I am eighteen, five-foot-six with long blonde hair, brown eyes, and slim build. I like reading – top three writers: Angela Carter, Charlotte Bronte, Paul Auster. I am going to Edinburgh Uni. I write (bad) poetry, love dogs and cats, and listen to all types of music, particularly British indie and Schubert's *Lieder*.' Her fingers stopped as she wondered about mentioning her skin. She could pose as a smooth-skinned girl. It might be fun. She could doctor her photo with Microsoft Photo Editor. She looked up at the ceiling, then back at the screen and started typing: 'Distinguishing marks?

I have psoriasis, about twenty-five per cent body coverage. Hurray!'

A man called Stewart mailed her. He was at Edinburgh already. 'I need to tell you straight off I got red hair. Yeah, I'm a ginger. What's psoriasis?'

They chatted regularly. He was doing engineering and lived in Berwick-upon-Tweed. He sent her more photographs of his house and family, and asked for ones in return. There were so few of Gemma, almost none since she was fifteen, since, well, since *it*. He said that if she was going up to look at Edinburgh, she should call him. She had planned to make a trip anyway, and went there to look over the department and check out her hall of residence. She telephoned him from her B & B in Morningside, and he suggested they meet up in a café near the National Library. He was tall and shy, with snaggleteeth and a lot of curly red hair. He took her to the Students' Union, and introduced her to a bunch of students sitting at a table. Nobody quite knew what to do or say. They ended up talking about where they went during their gap year. She was her usual chatty self but it felt odd – as everything in her life did. She was dogged by this feeling that she didn't fit in, she made people uneasy. It certainly didn't click with Stewart, and she walked back to her B & B on her own, stood at the window and watched the rain falling lightly in the glow of a streetlight.

Part of my own attempt to learn to live with psoriasis included finding a support group. I found a page on the web that said it could put me touch with my local psoriasis network. Apparently there were hundreds around the country. I typed

in 'WREXHAM' and it asked me for my state and zip code.
I could now understand the lure of the leper colony – and
I spent time in one in its modern incarnation: the websites
of the skin community. I found places where we can swap
stories and fulminate against the drug companies and dermatologists. Some have grown so large they have started to move
into new areas – legal advice, relationship tips, hotels that
tolerate flakers, and flaker creativity, which I closely inspected,
wondering exactly how bad a poet or a painter would have
to be to climb aboard the psoriasis bandwagon, the way
attention-hungry but untalented rock musicians end up turning
Christian to get a gig in church. But of course I now see
people who write on the subject of skin disorders rather
differently.

There were certainly poems and pictures that would be
unlikely to get an airing anywhere but a flakers' website, but
there were others that leapt off the screen. The psoriatic world
is evoked here by a woman called Ava, who describes it more
accurately than any medical textbook.

Catharsis
It claws into my heart
And maps my train of thought
And it's in the scratch of my fingertips
And in the tone of my voice
. . .
I'll give you something to stare at
look at me
Sweet red scales
Under a color-blind sky
Pick and peel it away

It feels so much better
When I'm looking at it on the floor
Or in my hands . . .
Forget the blood
Screw the pills and the tears
And the oil and the 'therapy' and the
sunlight
the stinging and sterilizing
My instincts and my predictability
I'll give you all something to gossip over
I'll give you all something to talk about
Pick it
Peel it
I.
Bleed.
Everywhere.
Leaving pieces of me behind
Wherever I go
    . . .

LET ME TELL YOU
That everything inside me
Is holding to the thought
That this is me
And it will never change.
Men become women.
Fat become thin.
And even the ugliest
Can Escape . . .
But this

This 'Temple of my mind'
Where the cuts and the pain
Take a back seat to
Humiliation . . .
This is home.

Washed up

It distorts us, sometimes beyond recognition as human beings. Joseph Stalin suffered from psoriasis. It does not surprise me. Jo – all is forgiven. I know what you were going through. You over-reacted perhaps a touch, but I understand the impulse to kill twenty million smooth-skinned people. Abimael Guzmán, aka Presidente Gonzalo of the Sendero Luminoso (the Shining Path guerillas), a political maniac from Peru, is also a psoriatic. He was ambushed by Government forces when he was sneaking into Lima for treatment. His plan had been to turn South America communist, but he has ended up rotting in jail. Yet another example of how psoriasis can spoil your dreams.

Only Gary, of all the sufferers I have met, managed fully to maintain his character and lifestyle in the face of psoriasis. He actually seemed to like his skin. He was always upbeat, but not like Gemma, through whose smile you could see the pain seeping. He made compromises – in what he wore and what sports he played and things like that – but it seemed his essential personality was not dimmed by it, the way mine was, the way everybody else's was.

'What would I do without my psoriasis?' he said to me.

'What husband – apart from me – is begged by his wife every year to take a three-week vacation on the beach in Jamaica? It's perfect. I thank God I have it. There's a downside, sure, but heck, I can handle it. And I guess you wouldn't fully understand the upside unless you have screwed Tina. I have. That's the difference.'

For the rest of us it is like living in an endless cloudy winter – something we are capable of, but something that is hard work and makes life grim. Our spirits do not soar – our joy is never unbounded. Bitterness and resentment gnaw at every experience. Our relationships are spoilt, our careers compromised. But the overriding difficulty is its relentlessness. It's like the posse chasing Butch Cassidy and The Sundance Kid – it has inexhaustible energy and yet never seems in a hurry. It never lets us go free, but it never quite catches up with up with us – it just keeps us running.

Even Howard couldn't escape – he had trudged drunkenly across the stone bridge outside the pub in Llangollen with the single thought of ending his life. The bridge that spans the River Dee in Llangollen is fifteenth century. The stone of its walls has been carved with the names of people who have passed over it for six hundred years. The drop on to the sharp rocks, over which the river skims, is thirty feet. In one place only the water has carved out a deep pool. This spot has been marked by the kids of the town by a V cut in the stone so they know where it's safe to leap from on summer days. In a stupor of sadness and beer, Howard chose exactly that spot, landed in deep water and was swept downstream on to the weir, where his large pendulous belly caught on the gravel bank and beached him. He opened his eyes, gasping for breath, looking up at the lights of the bridge and the town above him. He had failed to kill himself, but he smiled. 'Thank fuck for that,' he said, and stood up in his sopping clothes to make the unanticipated walk home to his cottage.

10

Yam Hamelah

A month never went by without somebody saying, 'I know how you can get rid of that . . .' or, 'My friend had that . . .' or, 'Have you tried x or y . . .?'

We skin people learn to tune out this conversation, to smile – even in extreme cases to take down the name of a drug or a therapy on a bit of paper (that we'll then bin), just to shut the person up.

But from time to time I weakened – and thus I found myself standing in line to check in at a hotel on the barren shore of the Dead Sea in Israel, waiting behind a guy with hands bandaged so thickly he couldn't hold the pen properly. He was wearing shorts, which seemed odd because his left calf looked like it had taken a burst from a sand blaster, and the bandage on his right knee seeped some ghastly fluid. Through the plate glass window the bone-coloured desert shimmered under the heat, and around me milled the most incredible collection of strange looking skins I had ever seen: mottled, marbled, brindled, florid, seeping, streaked, pocked and cracked, crimson, purple, deeply jaundiced and deathly pale. It was now official: I was a member of the ugliest community in the world.

It was the kind of hotel where you carry your own luggage, and upstairs the corridors were narrow and ill lit, the thin carpet ingrained with artificial sand and the air chemical, like a dishwasher opened mid-cycle. My room, 422, was mean and small, squeezed with hundreds of other identical ones into this honeycomb of unhappiness, this tower of misery. The thinly painted concrete walls seeped loneliness, pain and dashed hopes. The furniture was so cheap I could lift the bed with one hand, and when I moved it to make space to sit and write at the dressing-table, I found a piece of translucent human skin the size of a crisp. I held it between my fingers and coldly considered its implications.

The clinic was a ten-minute walk over a blasted landscape where nothing grew but my disgust and impatience. I had only agreed to go to the Dead Sea because I was aware how my psoriasis was spreading from my face and torso into my character, tightening my heart, and I didn't want people to think I wasn't trying to help myself. It's one of the features of psoriasis that people think it is our fault we have it, and that with only a little more effort we could rid ourselves of it.

Although I had a brief consultation with a dispiriting Russian doctor, he prescribed no drugs except for a bland moisturiser and a tub of salicylic acid ointment which was designed to soften the plaques. No cortisone, no vitamin D, no anti-inflammatory, no anti-cancer drug. All the therapy seemed to consist of was exposing myself to the sun, and this was accomplished on the hotel roof.

I will not forget the first morning I walked up there with my bed-sheet, bottle of water and book. Men and women were segregated by a blue polythene screen with little holes cut in it. I turned right and was faced with thirty naked men, all with spectacular skin problems. As a first-timer I was left alone to find my way through the misery of revelation, for stripping was invariably associated with disaster, but I felt everybody's eyes on me. Out of the corner of my eye I noticed that everyone else was much worse than me. There were guys so raw they looked like they'd been dipped in boiling oil, and vitiligo sufferers with skins like coloured ponies and Dalmatians. I chose a bed at the end of the line, and stripped off with the twin fear that I had psoriasis, and that I didn't have it badly enough.

But it was the kind of place where people cut you some slack. Stripping off is never easy, and to make matters worse, because psoriasis loves the nooks and crannies of the body, people had to lie in obscenely contorted positions to get the sunlight on them. One guy, whose skin was fully covered, by either tattoos or psoriasis, happily played draughts on all fours, head down, bum in the air, his buttocks cleverly parted with a cigarette lighter, so the sunlight – which was meant to be beneficial – shafted right down into his open crack. Some men lay on their sides with one leg waving in the air, and others lay on their back pulling up their scrotum and penis to stop them casting a shadow on the all important perineum, so often the command centre of the psoriasis invasion. We were the shyest people in the world performing like wild exhibitionists on a roof in Israel.

Fuck-Up Corner

It was in Israel that I met Gemma, as well as Bill, Marie and Emily Woodward, and heard their stories. Telling each other the narratives of our skins was, after sunbathing, the principal occupation of the guests at the hotel, and went on wherever we gathered, but particularly in the dining room, where we chattered away, radiating the heat we had absorbed during the day.

There were two tables in the corner furthest from the door, and therefore furthest from the outside world, where the worst afflicted dined. We were all rejects at the Dead Sea Hotel, but Fuck-Up Corner was where those who couldn't even cut it as rejects ended up. It was presided over by Fritz, a round-faced, gregarious German of about fifty, with tiny lashless eyes and a narrow white moustache. Grey hair grew in odd clumps from Fritz's neck, which like the rest of his body was mottled in blotches of pink, grey, mushroom and burgundy. The first time I saw Fritz I was standing at the buffet with a plate of food looking for a place to sit. Fritz was sitting between a man with a suppurating neck, pink eyes, no lips and bandaged hands, and, even more horrifyingly, on his other side, an empty seat. I pretended not to see Fritz's welcoming smile and beckoning hand, and ate at a table laid for one, looking hard at my food, afloat in the tank of human crustaceans that was the hotel dining room.

Each day I rose at dawn, trudged on to the roof, found a sunbed, applied my cream, sunbathed until about eleven, went for a siesta during the heat of the day, then dragged myself back up to the roof, going down to the swimming pool for a few lengths before dinner and finally clambering into bed, exhausted. On about the fourth day I noticed some changes on my skin. The generator of the skin cells seemed to have slowed, and where there had been long-established patches of dry skin, below my eyes, on my cheeks and nose, new healthy shiny skin appeared to be taking their place.

Please do not think I am about to claim that this therapy was in any way some kind of a cure. I think we know each other, and psoriasis, well enough to dispense with any of that kind of talk. I saw quite a few people for whom the Dead

Sea did nothing. But for me, and some of my fellow inmates – you couldn't call them guests in that place – there was a distinct improvement. But it was not just about my skin – it was also about the way I thought about myself, which for the first time seemed not to be directly connected with what I saw in the mirror.

The almost total absence of 'normal-skinned' people endowed the hotel with a magnificent, liberating atmosphere. Downstairs in the lobby, the freaks were in charge. Fritz waddled around reception in his Spandex trunks, belly hanging out, changing money and looking around for friends. Occasionally a healthy guest would turn up, maybe a family doing a tour of the Holy Land, and sit silently in the corner of the lobby looking aghast, and we all enjoyed making them, and not us for once, feel distinctly weird. We created a community where the standards of the rest of the world did not prevail. Perhaps it was not a coincidence that we were being looked after by Jewish doctors, nurses, waiters, cleaners and hoteliers. They seemed to understand what it was like to live a life that did not conform to the prevailing cultural standards, and never tried to burst the bubble we were all huddled inside.

For me and my skin, it was a kind of paradise, and by the end of the first week the agony of undressing passed, and I really didn't care about uncovering, let alone displaying, my body with all its flaws. I wanted to stop hiding myself for once. Physical appearance at the Dead Sea was an irrelevance. I lifted my head, something my neck told me I'd done for the first time in years.

The Dead Sea is in the world's greatest depression. It used to be fed by the River Jordan, though extraction has almost dried that up so nothing now replenishes it. Coruscating heat beats down and evaporates the water at an astonishing rate. The hotel used to be a waterside building. It would now stand half a mile back from the shore but for the bulldozers, which work round the clock to keep a lagoon of water in place. Because the sun has to travel through a kilometre of extra atmosphere, much of which is saturated by the chemicals caught in the sump of the Dead Sea valley, the spectrum of light that gets to the floor of the Dead Sea is unusual – and maybe it has some special properties that repel psoriasis. But the conditions were both harsh and kind. We could sunbathe in that ferocious light but not need sunblock. The air was so corrosive, and yet so emollient. No animals or plants could survive down there, but we band of psoriatics thrived.

The air smelled caustic, of perished rubber and elastic, but its effect on the mind was gentle and calming. Just inhaling it could soothe our skin. I know this not because some of the psoriatics improved on breathing it – that as we all know proves precisely nothing, psoriasis being so fickle. But there was another skin disease I saw for the first time at the Dead Sea called neuro dermatitis and the atmosphere had an astonishing effect on that. Seeing this girl Carla, a blonde German film-maker from Bremen, full of ND was one of the few times I thanked God I had psoriasis, because ND is far, far crueller. We said things like, 'Ah, good old psoriasis,' when we saw someone with ND.

A much rarer disease than psoriasis, neuro dermatitis tricked Carla so successfully into believing she was itching all over that she tore herself to shreds with her fingernails. I noticed that she had rubbed her wrists on the sides of her jeans so hard she had made two holes in the material. She had gone through both seams, that's four layers of denim,

148

double-stitched. And you should have seen the state of her wrists. They looked, like her in a way, like a madly bungled fucked-up suicide attempt. ND people looked like refugees, like people stripped of everything they ever owned and then hollowed out on the inside by self-doubt and creeping self-hatred. Always sleep-deprived, because their nails didn't stop attacking them even when they slept, they haunted the lobby like zombies with their thousand-yard stares.

Carla repeatedly made the ND salute of gently scraping the underside of her chin with her fingernails. She told me it was like a placatory gesture towards the disease inside her. If she failed to acknowledge its presence, it got angry and sulky and forced a deep scratching session on her. She also told me that the compulsion to itch was embedded so deeply in ND that a sufferer who was hit by a car and badly injured was still scratching himself while brain-dead in a coma he never emerged from. However, just two days at the hotel at the Dead Sea loosened ND's grip on Carla. She told me that all she had to do was lie on her bed and breathe lungfuls of air.

It was the magical soothing Dead Sea air that started Carla's healing, but the sun that really blew her neuro dermatitis away. The disease couldn't compete with its ferocious beneficial powers. Carla loved the Dead Sea sun in all its moods: at dawn when it was yellow, and hardly warmed the cool morning air as she spread her sheet and settled down with a book. A book! She could read now! She had grabbed that back from neuro dermatitis. Within an hour, as the roof began to fill with more naked female bodies, the light turned whiter, the shadows rapidly shortened and the heat started to build. By ten-thirty the sun warmed the juices in the marrow of her bones that oiled her joints and her skin. At midday she took a break in the shade by the pool downstairs, to return for another joyful blast in the afternoon, never missing the moment when with a starburst of orange the sun flashed its goodbye and disappeared behind the cliff at the back of the hotel.

I did the same and felt the cares of the world slip from my shoulders. At night, I telephoned friends I had not seen in months, if not years. I made contact with my family again – for some reason down at the Dead Sea they didn't seem the problem they did above sea level. I felt myself soften, like my skin, and come alive again.

Occupied territory

There was a war going on in Israel, but at the Dead Sea Hotel you wouldn't know it. I am sure the Israelis argued about it at their end of the solarium, but they never tried to involve us foreigners. From time to time a tight formation of F-16 jet fighters armed with red and white missiles rent the air over our naked bodies on the hotel roof, but when they returned thirty minutes later without the missiles no one asked where they'd been in the meantime.

Fritz looked up at them and said, 'Ze lucky fuckers. Zey vill be getting a good view of ze vomen's zolarium.' He had just invented a leather thong that ran round his neck, down his front and was attached with a little slip knot to the top of his todger. This way he got sun to that otherwise shady length of skin. It was extremely practical and quickly became a huge success in the men's solarium. When we lifted our heads to look at the F-16s, our willies simultaneously stood to attention for the fly past. But there was absolutely no sense that we were sunbathing on the worst political faultline in the world. We were indifferent to the sufferings of the Israelis and the Palestinians. We had bigger fish to fry than the Middle East crisis. We had a war raging on our skins, not thirty miles up the road in Palestinian Authority territory.

Down at ground level the only sign of the war was the Lebanese Red dope that the Israeli Defence Force guys stationed in the basement shared with us. They got it from friends in units in the security zone. I had rarely met less pugnacious men than the soldiers at the hotel. They spent their lives sunbathing by the pool, flicking through the fashion magazines the guests left and dancing in the disco. Admittedly, one of them was always on lookout in the machine gun nest on the cliff above the hotel, but that wasn't anything to do with watching for Palestinians. He was there to warn the guys if the Colonel drove down from HQ for an unscheduled inspection. And while he sat there he bided his time training the high-powered binos into the women's solarium.

The Israel/Palestine conflict wasn't the only dispute we ignored. Because the German Government, unlike the British, French or American ones (amongst many others), sent skin patients to the Dead Sea on their state health scheme, Germans were, after Israelis, the most populous nationality there. It was faintly disconcerting seeing so many naked Germans lying beside naked Jews, but we soon got used to it. Down there it didn't seem strange. When I went for my check-ups with the sad long-nosed Russian doctor I used to see the queue of anxious Germans on their first day waiting to have their heads shorn by the Israeli barber. Even Diego, a haughty Argentinian who had been decorated in the Falklands War, made friends with Roy, an English bigot, and taught him to play Piccolo Diccolo – a drunken game that involved pouring the ice bucket down their trousers and seeing who had the smallest willy.

We spent our time diagnosing each other, comparing skins, giving each other tips, and generally sympathising and bitching about life. A lot of this was done around the swimming pool, where people went for a cooling length or two after their grilling on the roof. It was at the pool that I first saw Bill, Marie and Emily Woodward, walking as though to the gallows through what was referred to as the garden but was in fact a few fly-blown oleanders clutching to life on a drip, and some squares of turf with their corners turned up like old sandwiches. The Woodward family were suited to the background. They did not look happy. Emily was in her full Goth regalia including white make-up and ankle-length coat, despite the forty-degree heat. Marie chose three sunbeds close to me, but Emily walked on and sat on one twenty feet away. Bill sat slumped on the end of the nearest, nearly tipping it up. His misery-laden stoop had been further rounded by disappointment and disillusionment – you could see he had nothing but contempt for the hotel. His eyes were dead and whenever Marie said anything he just tutted and looked away, ignoring her.

Emily was fifteen, and whoever hands these things out had decided to give her a dose of acne to deal with on top of everything else. She looked as though she was in Israel under duress, and if she even glanced in her parents' direction it was with searing contempt. When she took off her clothes there must have been thirty people pretending not to look. She was slim and pale, with dark eyes, shoulder length straight dark hair, and a circle of dead skin crawling out the back of her one piece the size of a dinner plate. It was bright red with a rim of flaky silver skin cells. She also had flaky calluses on her elbows where spots had bled, one that looked septic. There were other lighter areas on her thighs and her left shin, and that's not to mention what was hidden by her slack black bathing suit. She sat with hunched shoulders staring at the ground in front of her. I saw Bill suddenly look away – it wrung him out to see his girl like this.

When new people arrived they were soon befriended by one of the regulars – usually someone who had a similar type of psoriasis. A couple of guys in the solarium spoke to me about the kind of schedule I needed to maintain to clear my body, just as an Austrian woman called Petra, about Marie's age, with large plaques like Emily, approached the Woodward family and offered to take Emily on to the roof.

'Does she really need to go there?' Marie said.

'Of course – she has it under her bathing costume, no?'

'But she's not taking her costume off,' whispered Bill. 'The only bits that matter are the bits you can see.'

'I want to go up there,' said Emily.

'You better go with her, honey,' Bill said to Marie.

'No,' said Petra, taking Emily's hand (it was incredible to see how strong and fast the bonds between us skin people grew), 'you stay here, and let me take Emily with me.'

'Yes,' said Emily, 'I would like that.'

So Bill and Marie spent the days around the pool, sometimes looking up at the roof six floors above, where people, bored of lying down, wandered to the rail and looked out at the syrupy sea, which never formed waves or white caps, but lay there motionless below us, like we were looking at a photograph. In the long hot hours time sometimes seemed to grind to a comforting halt. The mind slowed and stopped and all those crazy anxious thoughts, which used to come pell-mell, were suspended. We went naked to the rail feeling the sun baking our shoulders, and stood on the hot tiles to catch a little breeze and look down at the amateurs, as people without skin problems were called.

I was told that things were a little different in the women's solarium – for instance, they helped each other apply oil. There was one tiny shrivelled old lady, a Holocaust survivor, encased in scales, called Lila, whom they all took turns to help with the salicylic. Over in the men's side there was no touching. You oiled up on your own.

On Emily's third day she and Petra rubbed oil into Lila.

'How does my back look?' Lila asked.

Emily was about to lie and say it wasn't too bad, when Petra said, 'It's not good my darling. It's not good at all. I'm afraid you are full of it this year.'

And Emily learnt – as I had – that nobody lied about skin at the Dead Sea. The reason? Because there was no shame in looking as we did – only shame attached to denying it. And she – like me – thought that was good.

But it was by no means all reassuring. I often gazed at the lines of crusty bodies, all splattered in what looked like blotches of dry candle wax and thought, That's my future, that is how bad it might get. And Emily didn't like being mothered by Petra, who treated her like a child. When Petra told her to start sunbathing at nine, Emily didn't show up until twelve, and as a result got so sunburnt she had to take a couple of days off. Petra came to her room.

'Emily, you are not here to play,' she said, 'this is work, and you must do as you are told or you will not get better.'

Emily lit a cigarette. 'Yeah – well, I'm sorry . . . whatever,' she waved Petra away.

'This is serious Emily, your mommy *und* daddy have paid a lot of money to bring you here.'

'I didn't ask them to.'

'You shouldn't smoke, you know,' Petra said, 'it is not good for your skin.'

'Leave me alone, can't you? What's it to you?'

'All right,' said Petra. 'I am only trying to help you.'

'Yeah? Well leave then.'

The most stared-at bit of glass in the world

There was a young woman there, a sun-drenched beauty of about twenty who delighted and cheered us all with her long blonde hair, brown eyes and satiny brown skin. When I first saw her at the pool in a bikini I could see she had no psoriasis, though the ghostly circles of slightly paler skin indicated where the sun had wiped it from her. She was now engaged in the final stage of the Dead Sea process – making her tan uniform. She walked so lightly, radiating joy, and every night her laughter pinged off the harsh concrete walls of the dining room. I never managed to force my way through her cordon of admirers to introduce myself, but one night, coming down in the lift, she stepped in from a lower floor. The doors closed and we both looked in the mirror. That lift mirror was the most stared-at piece of glass in the world. At different stages of our stay we looked at ourselves with all the emotions between outright suicidal despair and, as the healing weeks went by, glorious rapture at what seemed like our astonishing beauty.

'I used to hate doing this,' she said.

'Looking in mirrors?' I said.

'Instruments of torture,' she smiled, 'but now I can't drag myself away from them.'

'You look beautiful,' I said. You could say that – if it were true – and it was taken at face value, rather than as a come-on.

'You should have seen me four weeks ago,' she said. 'I was walking wounded.'

'I can see it's gone well for you,' I said.

'I feel happy for the first time in eight years. I can't tell you how amazing it is not to have to fake it!' she beamed. 'I feel like Sleeping Beauty.' The lift bell sounded as we slowed for the ground floor. 'I'm Gemma,' she said.

She launched herself into the lobby crowd. I took a last glance at the mirror. I remembered how painful mirrors used to be, but how they drew me back again and again. The cruellest mirrors were those circular magnifying mirrors which were more common in the seventies than now, but still findable. My mother-in-law had one, with a built-in light, which had an astonishing gravitational pull for me. I used to sneak to it as soon as I got into her house. It was an inquisition. What about this flap? I would try to pull it off. I'd rather have a raw bit of skin than a flapping patch. But now, as I followed in Gemma's wake, I ran my hand over my face and felt how smooth it was. A geyser of joy erupted inside me.

I glimpsed Gemma later squeezed up in an armchair beside Pablo, whom I knew from the roof. Pablo was a Spaniard afflicted with vitiligo. Some vitiligo people looked like they had had white paint thrown at them. Pablo only had one big patch on his body, over his genitals, otherwise it was just his knuckles and his knees. His therapy consisted of a heavy dose of the most intense Dead Sea sun, so he had to lie nude on his back right through the hottest hours when going out on to the roof was like being forced into a furnace, and everyone else was down by the pool for a shady lunch or in their rooms dozing. The idea was that this blast of sun woke up the bleached pigment and kick-started melanin production. It worked, but very slowly; meanwhile, Pablo's healthy skin turned first brown and then almost black, so his genitals, though no longer white, were relatively lighter than before he started sunbathing. Pablo's bizarre colouring was much admired by the jokers in the men's solarium.

Roy, holding his greasy pack of Benson & Hedges, stood in nothing but his flip-flops at the end of Pablo's sun lounger, the sunburst obliterating his head and torso.

'Relax, mate,' he said when Pablo articulated his fears about having sex looking the way he did. 'You've got nothing to worry about. You look fucking wonderful, mate,' he said, 'birds love that kind of thing once they get used to it. Forget novelty condoms, son, look at that: you got the ultimate sex toy there, an albino penis.' He proffered the greasy pack of Benson & Hedges.

People tended to group up in the solarium on the basis of language, but sometimes, with a minority affliction like vitiligo, they formed a disease ghetto. On both sides of Pablo lay other vitiligo sufferers pinned down on their loungers by the vicious sun. On his left was a forty-five-year-old Miami Cuban called Alberto, who lay on his side, one testicle peeping through his legs. His washed-out blue cotton sheet flapped in the breeze of the fan that wafted the desiccated newspapers from the Hebrew-speaking section all over the solarium. Alberto draped a hand-towel over a sunburnt buttock. He was trying to sunbathe a large white patch on his upper thigh without further burning his bottom, but the sun was so penetrating in the middle of the day there was nothing that could successfully shield a patch of sunburn.

Alberto had suffered from vitiligo for years. He got it when he was Pablo's age, about twenty-four. His first patches were on his knuckles and knees, but more soon appeared on his torso and arms. There was a period during his divorce when every time he looked at his skin he seemed to find a new area that was starting to de-pigment. It felt like aliens were taking over his body. He took oral and topical psoralens (the drugs that sensitise the skin to light), he changed diet countless times, threw back fistfuls of multivitamins, and used Dermablend or Covermark – medical cosmetics – to hide his whiteness, but nothing could repel the alien invasion. He was currently at about forty per cent body coverage of de-pigmented skin. When he got to fifty per cent he had the option to go on a new set of drugs that bleached the remaining normal skin and turned him all one colour again, albeit paler than the one he started with. The march of the disease was relentless. He watched Pablo working on his single pale patch. The poor guy had no idea of what he was going to go through over the next twenty years. Alberto closed his eyes and tried to think of something cheering. His good friend Gino, whom he had met ten years before on his first visit to the Dead Sea, always said, 'With vitiligo, Alberto, no matter where in the world you are, you always have a white Christmas.'

Pablo, sitting in the armchair with Gemma, looked at her closely. His wide eyes frankly said: You look great. It was a look she hadn't seen in years and years and she drank it up.

'How is your skin now?' she asked him.

'Okay.' He held out his forearm to her.

'Can I touch it?' she asked.

'Pliss. You see, it is nice.'

'Very, very,' Gemma agreed, letting her hand move up and down the back of his hand and forearm. 'Well done.'

'You come to disco, tonight?' he asked her.

'Not tonight,' she said, 'I want to get plenty of sleep and be at work early. My skin comes before having fun.'

Like the desert needs the rain

Petra used to do ten lengths every evening in the ochre light of the sunset. Emily sat with her black trousers rolled up paddling her feet in the water, watching her.

'Come in,' Petra said. 'It is good for your fitness level, *ja.*'

Emily said, 'No thanks'

'Nooo, come on – it is zo warm.'

Emily longed to do it, to just surrender and join in with the rest of us. She could have so easily slipped into the soft warm water and into Petra's open hands, which would have held her safely – but for some reason she didn't. The scales on Petra's body were as thick and large as Emily's. It looked like you could pick them off in big silvery discs, but Emily knew that if you tried it was red and raw underneath, because she'd often done it, just to hurt herself.

Emily reminded Petra of her own screwed-up childhood, when summer after summer she had had to think of excuses for why she couldn't go to swimming parties or to the beach. She saw Emily hesitate and knew exactly how hard it was for her to take off her clothes, get into the water and submit to the idea of letting go of the hardened child she had become.

Bill looked up from his book and said, 'She doesn't really do swimming.'

Wallowing in the shallows at the end of the pool, Petra said, 'Come on, Emily.'

'No thanks,' said Emily, adding quietly, 'I can't swim.'

It was the first conversation since Petra had been to her room, three days earlier.

Through the moisturiser-smeared glass door of the hotel, as though conveyed on air, wafted Gemma, her hair silvered by the sun, her face smooth and brown, her eyes alive with life, a sarong tied at her swinging hips.

'Gemma looked like you when she came, you know?' Petra said quietly.

Emily glanced at Gemma, without expression. 'So?' she said. 'Big deal.' She fumbled in her woollen shoulder bag.

'You have to work,' said Petra, her hand still out.

Emily took a Marlboro and lit it. Petra stepped back, and gently lowered herself into the lukewarm water, so only her head sat on the great flexible rectangle of the surface.

'You should swim, honey,' Marie said. 'If Petra says . . . '

'Leave her alone,' huffed Bill, then turned to his wife and lowered his voice. 'Look at her; she's miserable.'

Gemma lay beside Carla at the other side of the pool, drinking mineral water and talking quietly, while the skimmer flaps gulped beside them. In barely ten days Carla had been transformed. They had only known each other a week, but were firm friends. They made the most extraordinary couple – tanned and sun-drenched blondes, Carla with ice-blue eyes, Gemma with brown eyes.

They wore loose light garments that slipped off their shoulders often and easily, so you could see they were tanned all over their bodies. Nudity – or snatches of it – had a different value down at the Dead Sea. It was primarily dermatological and only vaguely sexual. I suppose after roasting on the roof we were all fully sated on nakedness. People had more sexual allure on the rare occasions you saw them clothed. During the day if you caught a glimpse of a bosom or a bottom all you did was evaluate it as an area of skin.

During the long hot hours on the roof, we revealed our scariest secrets to each other, knew each other's longings and desires, talked of all the many disappointments and humili-ations in our lives, and savoured each other's triumphs, no matter how small. I was deeply familiar with the lopsided shape of Gino's scrotum, the bottleneck in Fritz's todger, and every crease of Roy's sphincter.

Gemma had told Carla her secrets, particularly about her abject romantic history – and had taken the German girl into her trust.

'I have seen that many times,' said Carla, indicating Emily where she sat fully clothed across the pool. 'When the people come to the Dead Sea and for some reason do not want to clear the skin.'

'But why?' said Gemma.

'It is Emily's protection, it's what she's using to keep the world at a safe distance. It's so deep in her personality, maybe because she has had it from when she was a child. She looks frightened to think of herself without it. That's what I think. Change is such a challenge – even good change is difficult.'

Gemma glanced across the pool at where Emily was now hunched over her phone texting.

'Many people use their bad skin to protect them,' Carla said.

'From what?' Gemma asked.

'From having to have a relationship, or having to deal with some other problem, like weight for example.'

'She seems so angry,' said Gemma, 'like she's spiting us by refusing to clear.'

'Especially her father,' said Carla.

'Yes,' said Gemma. We had all seen how over-protective Bill was of her. 'She can love him and hurt him at the same time by not working. I can understand that, it's so complicated. She's trapped by her skin . . .'

'I am trapped not by my skin, but by the cure,' Carla smiled. 'I am trapped down here, in this place, this strange hole in the desert. You know, last year I spent five months here.'

'What?' Gemma sat up. 'Five months?' she repeated, aghast.

'I have to,' said Carla. 'Or my skin would have sent me insane. For sure. I think about killing myself too often when I'm up there.' She meant any place above sea level.

'But you look so amazing now,' said Gemma, and then suddenly stretched her arms in the air and cocked her wrists, throwing back her head and whooping. 'And so do I! Oh, it's so great!'

'Yeah, let's not talk about bad things. Tonight I am beautiful, and tonight we will party . . .'

Their laughter echoed around the swimming pool, which had emptied of people as the red dusk descended.

Carla had first been to the hotel when she was twenty-one; a year later, at the end of her third visit, she missed the bus back home and stayed on. During the quiet winter months, when the sun wasn't strong enough to face off psoriasis and the place went dead, she made brief trips out of the canyon to see friends or holiday, but the rest of the time she lived on the shore of the Dead Sea. When she was above sea level she couldn't keep her mind on anything but going back down there. Blasted, desiccated, dusty and dead as it was, to Carla it was a Garden of Eden and she was its Eve. Her eyes were a pale, shimmering blue, her irises, fully dilated in the intense sunlight, were so vivid and open and receptive. Her lips were full and pink, her teeth slightly curved.

She picked up the language. It seemed fitting to hear such an Aryan German speaking Hebrew there, where anything seemed possible. She made money working for the doctors and the hotels as a translator, and did a few shifts in the lobby shop selling jewellery and newspapers – though hardly anyone read the news. She had a room in a house over in Never Zoah, a community of workers' accommodation ten kilometres south along the white shore. Her few possessions were strewn on the tiled floor next to her slim mattress, but she didn't go there very often. There was a queue of people to love her and she mainly slept in their rooms at the hotel, but of course they always went home after a few weeks, so no one ever really got to know her. When one lover left on the transfer coach to the airport, she lay by the pool with an empty heart for a few days before hooking up with another.

That night in the lobby all eyes were on Gemma and Carla – except Bill and Emily's; the two Canadians sat in a huddle scowling. It was entertainment night in the lobby, and although everybody had so much to say, conversation became impossible when the dance band struck up.

The lobby gig at the Dead Sea Hotel was not the kind of engagement that performers had in their mind when they went into showbiz. Every Thursday the entertainment bus came down the winding road from Arad, the last town in the desert above sea level, with performers for the Dead Sea Hotel.

If the bus crashed on one of the precipitous corners it would not make the showbiz gossip columns or produce any star-studded funerals.

A short, demoralised old man with a comb-over wearing a filthy bell boy's tunic with shiny shoulders and stained trousers stood uncertainly by a drooping microphone, his huge head bent with worldly cares as he sang, 'Start spreading the news . . .' Beside him, a ludicrously tall and thin synth player stood with his top button done on his shirt and a tarnished sax hanging from his neck like an albatross. They broke into a formulaic 'Que Sera, Sera', but brought real conviction to 'If I Were a Rich Man', to which an Israeli with a prosthetic leg joyfully danced staring into the eyes of a French woman whose plump arms were decorated in a tracery of silvery plaques of psoriasis.

When the music drew to a barely co-ordinated halt, everyone clapped extravagantly because clapping extravagantly was so enjoy-able. Many years of lobby entertainment taught the professionals that lowering your expectations was a perfectly efficacious way of having them met. But when the singer came off the band-stand, people moved away from him, scared of getting ponced for a drink. Only Fritz, who had to be the friendliest man on earth in order to get any social interaction at all, main-tained the heroic eye contact he had kept up throughout the number.

'Encore! Bravo Bravo!' he shouted. 'Superbo! You are our Frank Sinatra,' he said in English, clapping his sloping shoul-ders. 'This is our Caesars Palace! Now. After a show like that, we must celebrate! What are you drinking?'

'You must come to the disco tonight,' Pablo said to Gemma.

Gemma said, 'Why?'

'Because if you come you will make everyone feel beautiful, and the whole disco will dance.'

She smiled. 'Well I suppose I must, then,' she said.

At around midnight the lobby bar closed and Gemma grabbed her last chance to delight herself in the lift mirror while they descended to the basement. Then they took two more flights of stairs down to the nuclear shelter at the very bottom of the hotel. The disco was like the most ordinary small town disco imaginable: a low ceiling, stale air, a dancefloor with large coloured lights lamely flashing out of time, a sticky carpet that led to a few soft banquettes in the gloom, a booth for the DJ and a bar with the barmaid on the edge of a nervous breakdown holding drinks in both hands screaming at guests to get their attention.

The playlist in the disco was peculiar. The DJ, a lifeguard by day, had put together a collection of records about the sun, the desert and skin. As the disco began to fill you could always here the sparkly melody of 'Here Comes The Sun'. Later we danced to 'Your body, my body, everybody wants my body,' and to Lloyd Cole's 'Perfect Skin'. The quality of the music was variable, but nothing ever seemed ordinary in the disco. In there even the cruddiest music sounded so sweet, so on the nail, so very hip, so danceable, but then the Dead Sea Hotel euphorics would have boogied to a road drill.

Generally, people with skin diseases aren't big dancers because we don't want to draw attention to ourselves, and anyway feel too ugly to move so freely, but at the Dead Sea disco we all let ourselves go. And many who at home were confirmed wallflowers felt for the first time that they could dance beautifully, groovily well. Gemma closed her eyes and smiled transcendentally, simply happy to be alive, simply *to be*, for once in her life. Under the UV, the luminous dials of our wristwatches, intensified by the hours in the sun, glowed with eerie power like their owners. Even a man who had arrived ten days before from Moscow in a wheelchair managed to stagger around from pillar to pillar feeling like Fred Astaire.

I've kicked the habit (kicked the habit, kicked the habit),
sang Peter Gabriel
SHED MY SKIN (SHED MY SKIN, SHED MY SKIN),
This is the new stuff (is the new stuff, is the new stuff),
I go dancing in, we go dancing in.
Oh won't you show for me (show for me),
And I will show for you . . .

It was as though a long, horrible, poisonous war had, that night, been declared over. It was like a huge win for a lottery syndicate. All of us: men, women, girls and boys, dancing in most cases on our own or in loose groups, exulted, at last, at bloody last, in ourselves. We were a room full of sleeping beauties who'd been woken by a kiss from the sun. We danced driven by lust and by love, but mostly by friendship and our new found affection for ourselves.

I touched my nose. I ran my fingertips over my cheeks. I felt no hard skin. I was a person again.

Gemma watched Pablo on the floor. He danced on his own with his back to her, wearing trousers so loose she could see the curve of the top of his ass. She thought, I need to dance with him again, just as Pablo twisted round and gazed unambiguously at her. She was so happy. She was back on the floor. Pablo kept getting closer. Her life was saved. His mouth was so kissable and near her neck. 'Like the desert needs the rain,' urged the singer.

Pablo led her upstairs, kissed her in the lift, took her room key from her loose hand and let her into 507. The curtains were open and the silver moon on the surface of the ever-calm Dead Sea filled the dark room. This was the moment Gemma had been waiting for: she undressed and stood in front of him. Undressing was such joy at the Dead Sea. She had had so much practice at it on the roof, where every inch of her skin begged for sunlight, that she learnt to love the feeling of clothes slipping from her skin. And her clothes seemed to want to get off her as much as she wanted to be naked.

They proceeded to have sex while Marvin Gaye, deep in the basement, moaned, 'Baaaaby, I got sick this morning,/ A sea was storming inside of me,/ Baaaby I think I'm capsizing,/ The waves are rising and rising,/ And when I get that feeling,/ I want sexual healing . . .' Gemma exulted in it. Every centimetre of her body was smooth and brown and healthy, she had not a worry in the world and she felt for the first time in her life absolutely, undoubtedly, without any fear, incredibly wonderfully wildly sexy.

On the days that followed, when they weren't on the roof, Pablo and Gemma locked themselves in 507 and drew the blackout curtain that produced a constellation of stars when the sun shone through the tiny nicks where the chemicals had eaten the rubber. They ate dates and drank mineral water sitting cross-legged on the bed listening to music. Pablo looked at her as though she were the most astonishing human being he'd ever set eyes on. Time meant nothing; they made love, they napped, they made love, they talked, they talked, they made love, they napped. They could only tell if was day or night by the stars that came out in the day. At night they went on foot into the desert and faced the beating wind by the silver sea. Pablo was in love. And Gemma looked like a goddess. She was the beauty of the hotel – silver hair, pink lips so well defined, and brown eyes that had suffered but had overcome.

Bye-bye Bill

When Fritz came on to the roof, it was obvious he was a true professional – a regular of many years' standing. He strode on to the solarium as if it were the sundeck on his motor-cruiser. He held his head high, the early morning breath of wind ruffling his tuft of neck hair, a confident smile on his face, despite his mottled body being sheathed in scales.

'Yitzhak – you okay man? Joe, cool. Edwin, yes. Gino, *ciao*, Roy, Tex, *wie geht's*? Brezhnev, Diego, Greek boy, Carlos, Pablo . . .' and hellos and *shalom*s and *hola*s and *ciao*s and all rights blossomed all round him. Having tucked sheets round his tan-wagon, laid out his oils, Walkman, backgammon set and Thermos of iced water, Fritz peeled off his shirt.

'What the, what the hell is that?' Roy said, aghast, sitting up on his elbow.

Fritz ignored the remark and started rubbing handfuls of oil into his body.

'That contagious?' Roy said. 'You mind lying somewhere else? You are full of it, man, you are shite. But not as bad as me.'

'*Ja*,' said Fritz, 'it looks like this year is a vintage one.' He looked down at his shins and brushed off excess scales. 'I have some work ahead of me.' With that he lay down, looked up at the sun and started sunbathing.

Fritz cadged so many of Roy's duty-free Benson & Hedges that Roy substituted the matchbox with which he kept his buttocks apart for his cigarettes, hoping it would put Fritz off. But when Roy turned over on to his front, Fritz got off his bed, gave a little chuckle, and said, 'As you say in England, do you mind if I bum a ciggie?'

The mornings always passed slowly. I used to look at the clock, drop my head on to my folded arms, gasping for breath in the heat, and lie for what seemed like an hour, before checking the clock again and seeing that five minutes had elapsed. By midday, the solarium started thinning out. The new people, with their pale skins, and those men who just couldn't lie in the withering heat and inexorable sunlight for one more minute of one more day without going demented, were driven downstairs into the air-conditioning and shade. Those deep-brown bodies that remained, whose psoriasis became silver edged in the brightness, lay listlessly amongst the empty, flapping sheets. Desiccated Israeli tabloids skidded across the floor and blew around the unoccupied mattresses. The light was so bright everything glowed like a negative. Men lay like dying animals on their beds, slugging at water as if it were oxygen.

It was during a blazing midday session that Fritz gave me a master-class in using moisturiser. I had been issued with a plastic tub of what was called Eucerin cream, about the size of a jam jar. I thought it would last me about two months, maybe more, and applied it from the end of my forefinger, smearing it lightly over any dead or dry skin, and avoiding any healthy skin.

'*Nein, nein!*' called Fritz, standing up and wandering towards me. There were some magnificent genitals on display on the roof, but I personally admired Fritz's pug-nosed cannon with its two fat wheels the most. 'This is how we apply the cream,' he said. 'Use three fingers, not two, not one, to extract the cream.'

I did as I was instructed. 'That's far too much,' I exclaimed.

'Zat is sufficient for one leg maybe,' he said. 'Now. Apply it.'

I larded on the grease, and felt my hands swimming over my flesh.

'One pot – one day,' Fritz said, 'understand?'

I used the whole pot then and there, and lay basting like a turkey. My skin drank it in, and that night, after my shower, I possessed a sheen I had only ever admired on others. I thought about why I had always been so sparing with cream. With prescribed ointments I always told myself it was because I didn't want to go back to the doctor for more, but I'd even been stingy with Nivea and baby oil. It was because I associated the need for oil with weakness, and the use of it with indulgence. This went back to Kennaway family myths which stated that a Kennaway never needed help, and never asked for it, because Kennaways were survivors. There was also this idea in my head that only inferior skins – particularly Mediterranean and Middle Eastern ones – required oiling, a process which could quite possibly rot the character. Good old white skin needed nothing more than a stinging splash of aftershave. The great white men of the Empire – Cecil Rhodes, David Livingstone, Winston Churchill – were not moisturisers because they possessed the best skin in the world, which of course required no outside help.

But it turned out that my skin was just thirsty, and when I let it drink, it consumed a ridiculous volume of baby oil and Eucerin, and over a course of a week transformed from papery and brittle into supple and fresh. I am now never without a bottle of oil of some kind for my skin, and accept that even healthy flesh needs care, and that giving it attention does not make me some kind of spineless narcissist.

I was down at the pool after a day's work, when I saw Bill and Emily decide to pack it in and go back to Vancouver. Marie was still praying that things would change and Emily would start to get some benefit. While her husband and daughter blanked everybody, she nervously smiled, though the problem was that the occupants of the hotel had turned against the family when Emily set her heart against trying. We were uncomfortable with Emily's reminder of just how horrible psoriasis is. We had created this fantasy that we were normal, nay beautiful, people, who occasionally were afflicted with bad skin, and Emily burst that bubble with her pancake make-up, black clothes and contemptuous stare.

As usual, the Woodward family arrived at the pool around mid-afternoon, Bill's features set in fury with the people he saw lying around the place. Usually he sat fully clothed in the searing heat, hunched on the end of Marie's sunbed, his eyes screwed up against the glare, but now at least he was in swimming trunks. Marie, carrying a swimming bag, strode out ahead, grimly making the best of the situation.

There was another family of mum, dad and daughter – an American girl seven years younger than Emily, with a shaven head covered in red polka dots, called Dee. As Bill and Marie walked beside the pool, Dee's mum and dad appeared through the glass door behind them.

Dee called out from the shallows, 'Dad, Dad! Watch me! I can swim! I can swim! Watch me!'

Gemma and Carla had been teaching Dee to doggy-paddle, and stood in the water and clapped as she spluttered from one to the other. Then she rushed out of the water, past Bill and Marie, to her parents. Her mum looked at her. The towel fell from her hands.

'Look, look,' she said to her husband, 'look.' She pointed at Dee's slim back. 'Look, hon. It's getting better. Right here.' She rubbed her hand on Dee's head and saw that no flakes came off. Her husband looked.

'It's definitely getting better,' Dee's mum smiled. 'Oh baby, I'm so pleased,' she tried to hug her daughter. 'Oh, my little baby, you are getting better. Give Mom a hug, come on.' Tears flooded down her face as she held out her arms to her little girl. 'You're gonna be all right . . .'

'Get off me, Mom,' Dee said and slipped out of her grasp to run back to the water.

'Oh hon, she's going to clear,' Dee's mum said to her husband, squeezing his hand.

'Yeah,' I heard Bill say under his breath to Emily, 'but for how long? I heard it comes back a week after you leave here, and it comes back worse.'

'I hate it here,' Emily said, 'everyone's so freakin' corny. I want to go home.'

'She wants to go home, Marie.'

Marie was wistfully watching Dee in the water. She said nothing.

'Right. We're leaving,' said Bill. 'I'm going to check out tickets and refunds. This place is a failure. Look, they come every fucking year. Of course it doesn't work. Some of them have been here *twenty times*, and they still look shit.'

I last saw Bill at reception trying to negotiate a refund for leaving early. Apparently they took a taxi to the airport at Tel Aviv in the middle of the day when the lobby was quiet.

Usually people left at breakfast time. A big crowd always gathered to see them off, and I watched many friends boarding the bus. It was like waving them off to war. People said they were going home, but it felt like they were leaving home.

Niveau de la mer

I sunbathed every hour I could for my last few days, trying to fill myself to the brim with the sun's golden elixir. While I was up on the roof I started talking to some of the Israeli guys about their war with the Palestinians. There was a spectrum of opinion, from the 'There will only be peace when we have security, and we will only get security when we beat them in battle' to 'If we could just create enough links to develop cultural and economic programmes together we can learn to share the country and live in peace.'

In an oil-stained *Jerusalem Post* I read about the attempts at brokering peace in the Oslo Accords, and studied the proposed map of Israel and Palestine that the Accords were supposed to bring into reality. There was something I couldn't put my finger on that was familiar about it. Then I realised what it was – the map looked like Yitzhak, an ancient emaciated Jewish guy who had folds of loose skin that from the front made him look the same shape as Israel. His neck and shoulders were the Lebanese border, the slender V of his crotch was the Negev desert, his pendulous penis a credible Red Sea, one leg the Sinai and the other the Arab Peninsula. All over both the map and Yitzhak were circles of pink, which on the map were proposed autonomous Palestinian communities and on Yitzhak plaques of psoriasis.

I was very pleased with my comparison, but kept it to myself.

The hotel wasn't the kind of place where you started a provocative conversation. All of us had spent too long trying to calm thoughts sent racing around our brains by psoriasis. But as I watched Yitzhak trying to burn those plaques off, and heard how, like the rest of us, he had tried all kinds of solutions in the past, I couldn't help thinking how similar the war and the disease were. Both alternated aggressive attacks with periods of calm and peace. Both promised a solution but never achieved one. It made me think that psoriasis was the manifestation of some ancient unsolvable enmity which for some reason had chosen my – and others – skin to fight its unwinnable war on.

Pablo – the love of Gemma's life – went home to Seville, and Gemma was sad. For thirty-six hours. Two nights later she met a guy from Italy called Raffi, a tall, toned and handsome man with patches of psoriasis on his legs and buttocks. Time was tight so they rushed through the preliminaries and were soon having a torrid affair.

It was during Raffi that Gemma got the idea not to go back to Surrey. She didn't have to be in Edinburgh until October, she had nothing else planned for the summer and she was sure Chrissie would help her with the money. She wanted to become, like Carla, a mermaid of the Dead Sea, and live down there where she thrived.

We were due to leave on the same bus, but Gemma told me the night before, in a lobby full of guests of the most incredible hues, squawking in a score of languages, that she was staying on.

'I can't leave,' she said, 'I can't. It's too amazing here. Look at me, for goodness' sake! I'd be mad to leave!'

I packed my bags at dawn. The sun I loved came up on the Dead Sea and filled my hotel room with its pale yellow light for the last time. I could hear the bass of the disco, the hotel's heartbeat, still pounding. I bid my concrete box of a room farewell, as if it were a rare and exquisite chamber. Tears formed in my eyes for its thin bed with the grey counterpane, its stained armchair and broken curtain. The lobby was filled with people in pyjamas and bathrobes who had risen to say goodbye to the few of us who were fully dressed.

Petra, in a tweed suit, must have had twenty people crowding round her. I saw her kneel down and take a glowing, carefree Dee in her arms, close her eyes and whisper something into the little girl's ear. Fritz got off the sofa, still dressed from the disco as he'd crashed out in the lobby to be certain not to miss us, and staggered over to shake my hand and write my number and address down in his dog-eared address book. He gave me his on a dimpled paper napkin.

I was surprised to see Gemma, with her packed bag. A queue of waiters, bar staff, and guests of varying ages formed a line to kiss her goodbye, a couple of them going round twice for a laugh. I went out to the coach and slung my bag into the hold, then came back to feel the arms of my friends round my neck one more time.

Raffi gave Gemma a kiss. '*Ciao bellissima.* You look after yourself, hear?' he said, turning away. She held on to his hand, then let his fingers go.

We piled into the coach. I had positioned myself near the back, and Gemma came and sat next to me, radiating beauty. We pulled away from the crying faces and the waving arms. When, after half an hour of driving uphill, the coach toiled past the sign on the side of the road that said NIVEAU DE LA MER I felt like I was resurfacing from an underwater dream-world.

'I didn't think you were coming,' I said to Gemma.

'I wasn't going to.'

'What made you change your mind?'

'Carla spoke to me last night. She said, "Get on that bus or you'll lose your life . . ."'

She looked out at the desiccated wadi and the empty land beyond.

'She's right,' Gemma said. 'If I'd stayed it would have been another victory for my psoriasis, you know?'

11
Madness and Badness

In the airport at Tel Aviv I went straight to the toilets, glanced at the lights, assessed their influence, and moved into the mirror. Deterioration started straight away for some people; I had been above sea level for three hours and was doing my first check to see if the sunshine, the oil and the strange magic were draining out of me now I had resurfaced in the real world.

Breathing fast on anxiety, I inspected every square millimetre of my face, giving careful attention to my eyelashes and my hairline, where often the first tiny peelings that spread to my cheeks and nose showed. There was nothing there. Actually, there was something there – there was *me*. And after two more checks at the airport, two in the aeroplane (difficult because aeroplane toilet tinted mirrors are so flattering), one at the Passport Control toilets at Heathrow, more over the course of that night, the next day and into the following week, I began to notice other features in my face – my nose, my eyes, my lips and my teeth, things I had never bothered to register before.

Weeks went by, and then months, without me seeing any psoriasis or finding any flakes of skin in my keyboard or on my shoulder. I had spent so many years brushing dandruff from my jacket I must have had abnormally developed triceps. But I didn't need to do it any more. I looked like a normal person with normal skin. Yet I didn't feel normal. It took months before I stopped thinking every day when I got up and every night when I undressed I was going to find some hard dry red skin.

It felt as though my sight had been restored. I had been so scared of facing life I could describe every pavement style in London, and knew every pair of shoes my friends wore, but that was about all I had seen of the world. There were so many people and places I had been avoiding – and they all now needed to be visited and stared at, long and hard. In addition I had an urge to show myself to the world, before my satiny skin was taken away from me, so I was in a hurry.

I gazed into people's eyes, no longer scared of seeing pity or even disgust. I adored being in company, revelling in the fact that there wasn't the unspoken thing between us to spoil the encounter. And had it all stopped there, I would have been a well-adjusted, happy, healed man. But it didn't.

The black lake

Now on his way to Jerusalem, Jesus travelled along the border between Samaria and Galilee. As he was going into a village, ten men who had psoriasis met him. They stood at a distance and called out in a loud voice, 'Jesus, Master, have pity on us!'

When he saw them, he said, 'Go, show yourselves to the priests.' And as they went, they were cleansed.

One of them, when he saw he was healed, came back, praising God in a loud voice. He threw himself at Jesus' feet and thanked him – and he was a Samaritan.

Jesus asked, 'Were not all ten cleansed? Where are the other nine? Was no one found to return and give praise to God except this foreigner?' Then he said to him, 'Rise and go; your faith has made you well.'

(Luke 17: 11–19) New Guy Kennaway Version

Often known as the Story of the Thankful Leper, the question arises – what happened to the other nine? My theory is that they looked at their skins, pinched themselves, jumped up and down with joy and ran into town for some fun. No time for spiritual growth, no time for any thanks. Time to party.

Nine months had passed since the Dead Sea with no sign of our old friend reappearing, and I was now drunk on joy. I didn't think I was just healed, I thought I was absolutely gorgeous, and swaggered around as if I had the secret of eternal youth in my pocket. The whole world, including me, seemed ineffably beautiful. It was as though I had a top Hollywood director of photography lighting my life. The colours were so vivid, the teeth so white, the smiles so warm, the eyes so seductive. Sometimes when I spoke to total strangers it felt as though we had the most sublime connection, and when I looked at them I could almost see stars twinkling around their heads. Everybody looked gorgeous; the whole world was endlessly exciting and enticing. I threw myself into it, glorying in everything.

But I am afraid to report that things were, even then, still not quite right about me. For a good few of my psoriasis years I had been aware of a shadowy darkness close to me, though I didn't know quite what it was. It felt like I was standing beside a deep black lake, whose water was both scary

179

and enticing. I had touched it and knew it to be dangerous and knew I shouldn't be there. The water wasn't alcohol or drugs or depression or gambling – it was sex.

It's hard to describe exactly what was going on in my head, because I can't really understand it myself, even now, looking back at it from a *relatively* sane perspective. Maybe because I had denied myself any pleasure in my appearance for so long – when really there hadn't been *that* much wrong with me (compared to Fritz, for instance) – I now went to the other end of the scale and believed myself to be absolutely beautiful and irresistible to all and sundry. Particularly sundry. Socrates said the male libido was like being chained to a madman. In my case the chain broke and I was the madman.

The details of the next few years are far too sordid to leave out of a modern memoir, but I am going to go against fashion and resist using my own crazy behaviour to titillate the reader. My idiotic sexual shenanigans were destructive enough at the time – for my wife, my children and all the others who were caught in the flying shrapnel of my increasingly ridiculous behaviour – and to recount them, under the guise of openness, only makes me more exploitative.

Think of the worst drunk you know – and replace the bottle with sex – that was how it got for me. The confused and contorted mental and emotional demands of what I was up to left little head space for the present. Nearly all of my thinking was either crawling guiltily over the past or drooling about the future. I drifted across that black lake further from the shores of sanity, and either could not or did not swim back. My legs were caught in straggling weeds and my arms were tired, but it always seemed safer and easier to swim on than turn back to the shore and get out.

Gary doesn't get it

Psoriasis is not finished with us when it is no longer visible. It says to us, You can get me off your skin – but I'm still here lurking inside you. I can take many forms to control your life.

With Gary, it had to absent itself to hurt him. In the autumn of 2000 he didn't get his expected attack of psoriasis, and Annette, seeing him in the shower, said, 'Honey, your skin is so good, you won't have to go to Jamaica this year. Isn't that amazing? You can come hiking with me and the kids.'

It was traditional for Annette to take the kids to Yosemite with her outwardly bound, puritanical mother for ten days of bracing exercise and general self-denial while Gary was in Jamaica. It was not Gary's kind of gig.

When he got to the office he called Tina and told her that for the first time in ten years he might not be able to make it.

'But Gary,' she murmured, looking around her realtor's office in Naples to check no one was listening, 'this can't be so. I am so hot for you, I can't sleep.'

'Yeah, and I want you too, sugar, you know I do. But if I stay clear there's no way I can get away. Annette won't wear it, I'm sorry.'

He finished the call and spent the morning daydreaming about Tina's compact body. He forgot about work. The business could get along without his attention these days. He had come to so dominate the movie catering business that his one ambition left was to persuade the Academy to institute an Oscar for best catering and win it.

He couldn't sit still – he was angry to be denied Tina, and

miserable that he was not going to be able to slake his appetite on her hot hard body, something he'd been thinking about, on and off, for months. He rolled up his chinos to inspect his ankles: the little blond hairs rose from unblemished flesh. He felt stressed – but that was good, he argued. It could bring on his psoriasis sufficiently to justify a trip to Jamaica.

Annette was always telling him to quit drinking red wine, because she'd read somewhere it made psoriasis worse, so he dropped by a liquor store on Sunset Boulevard and picked up a mixed crate of the cheapest red wine in the store. He tried to remember what else she said.

Her voice sounded in his head, 'Gary, what are you doing with that on your plate? Put those peppers back straight away. Really. You should know better.' Peppers, and tomatoes. They were bad for you. It was coming back.

It was only in desperation, like so many other sufferers, that he began to think about diet being its cause. He went and bought a book called *The Psoriasis Diet*, didn't read it, but flicked through until he found a list of dos and don'ts. He made a list of the don'ts: cream, cheese, eggs, alcohol (especially red wine and port), yeast, lemon juice, vinegar and a few other things, and went to the supermarket and bought the lot. When he got home he went to the kitchen. Annette was out chauffeuring the boys from one place to another. Gary made himself a cream, cheese, salami and lemon eight-egg omelette, swigging from the cheap red wine as he worked. He dashed the food down, and rolled up his trouser leg. Nothing. Well, it would take time.

'But you do not have much time,' he mouthed to himself in the mirror. He had to leave for Jamaica in a few months, and there wasn't a scale on him. He longed for the familiarity of suite 404 at the Negril Beach Club and the novelty of Tina's body. He longed for his Jamaican friends – the waiters, domestics and front-of-house staff whom he'd known for so many years.

He decided to ring me in England.

'Gary, you seedy reprobate,' I said to him, 'what can I do for you?'

He told me his predicament. I laughed.

'How are you doing?' he asked.

'Fine,' I lied. I wanted to tell him about what I was up to; after all, I couldn't think of a more sympathetic person on the subject of adultery than Gary, but something made me shut up. It was like I once again had someone inside my mind, commenting on my life, giving advice (bad advice) and making plans for me, the way psoriasis had in the past. Perhaps it was still psoriasis, mutated into a new form, finding a new way to ruin me.

'I am going to give myself a dose of psoriasis if it's the last thing I do,' Gary said. 'So, I need some advice. How am I going to get an outbreak?'

'Get some stress in your life.'

'That's good,' he said.

'And take drugs, nasty ones, in large quantities.'

'I'll give that a try. I'll keep you posted.'

From time to time he'd ring or email me with the latest developments in his campaign. I encouraged him, because I justified my own increasingly weird behaviour by comparing it to Gary's. But Gary was different from me. For a start he was truthful to me, but I was telling him nothing.

He addressed the problem of drugs and stress at the office the following week. He phoned a dealer and ordered up some coke. After he'd dropped off the kids he got to his desk and spent the morning swigging three-bucks-a-bottle Mexican Cabernet, and eating tomatoes from the tin. He was hungry and actually wanted a bean-shoot salad and pita bread, but ruled them out on health grounds.

Gary was due to place an order for a new catering wagon that week. At $508,750 it would absorb all the available cash in the business, but after a lot of soul searching with his partner, the cautious Bud, the two of them had decided to go for the purchase, and hope they got the work to justify it later. He picked up the phone and ordered not one new bus but four, total cost $2,035,000. He then faxed the bank with a transfer for ten per cent of the figure for a down payment. They had two months to come up with the $1,831,500 balance, or they'd lose the $203,500. When the transaction was completed he opened the desk drawer and snorted a thick line of coke off a photograph of Tina.

The full enormity of what he had done only hit him when later in the day the door flew open and Bud, usually a quiet, bookish man, tore in and said, 'Just what the flaming heck are you up to, Gary? Have you totally lost your mind this time? We said one new vehicle, not four! Jesus! You're going to bank-rupt us!'

'Hold on a moment, Bud,' Gary held up his hands, nipped into the bathroom and took a quick look at his reflection. He positively glowed with good health. What the hell had gone wrong with his skin – or rather what the hell hadn't gone wrong?

Gary knew exactly how clever psoriasis was.

'If you allow it the upper hand you are finished,' he told me by email. 'Whatever we try to do with our lives, it will spoil it for us, you know? This is one fight I will not walk away from.'

Bud spent the next days frantically working the phones trying to rustle up bookings, drivers and cooks for their new enlarged fleet. Gary had no intention of trying to dig them out of the hole he'd got them into. Instead he sat at his desk leafing through invoices, adding up how much he and Bud owed. It was now a terrifying amount. He soaked up the stress. He took more coke. Then he phoned the coke dealer.

'Hey, Caterine, you know that snowy stuff you got me?'

'You want more?'

'Yeah, I need five more grams.'

'Hey, cool it on the phone, man, cool it. You want to meet?'

Gary contemplated getting caught up in a drugs bust. A humiliating appearance in court to request bail. Police shots holding his charge number in the local newspaper. That's just the kind of thing that would play havoc with his skin. But it was too complex to organise. And he'd probably have to get jailed to get psoriasis.

'I need two more grams, but not the same quality.'

'Hey, man, that shit's the tops, it's fuckin' pure shit, man, uncut, you won't get better than that.'

'I know. I need something a bit lower grade, a bit more jagged, cheap and speedy.'

Gary was so drunk on his way back home after swigging Mexican Cabernet all day he nearly hit the garage – not that that did anything for his skin. What he needed, he told me, was a real shock, a situation quite beyond his control. The investment at the office – it wasn't really fundamentally traumatic. What was the worst that could happen? Bud quit? The business go belly-up? So what, he could handle it. He was Gary Speed, it was Los Angeles, anything was possible. He'd probably start another business and make even more money. Pressure? Who was he kidding? Evidently not his psoriasis. No, he had to perpetrate an outrage – then the psoriasis would flare. It was too clever to fool easily.

The next morning, after Annette left for work with the kids, Gary had an idea. He went through to the kitchen where Judy, the *au pair* from New Zealand, was clearing up breakfast. Judy was a big girl, large of thighs and feet but small of bosom and eyes, whose friendly ugly face had received precious little love from men.

'Judy, may I have a word with you, please,' Gary said.

'No probs,' said Judy gamely, and followed Gary down the corridor towards Gary's bedroom.

'In here, please,' he said. Judy walked in and smiled warmly. 'Judy, I guess you've noticed how over the past few months since you've been with us, I have fallen for you.' He took her hands. They were rough from the hard manual labours Annette set her to.

'Jeez, Gary, well, no, I had no idea.'

'Well, I do, I really feel strong about you and me.' He kissed her hands. They smelt of the kitchen cloth. He brought her big body towards him. 'Mmm,' he murmured, and started kissing her. It didn't take long to get her clothes off and have her in his and Annette's bed. Annette's bed! It was absolutely terrifying. If Annette found out, there would be, well there would quite possibly be murder, but there would also be . . . sweet bliss, psoriasis.

'What ibout a pricaution?' Judy managed to murmur, at some point. Gary stopped, tried to remember if he had any condoms in the house. Then he thought, No, crank it up, Gary.

'We don't need one of those. If you get pregnant, let's have the baby.'

When it was all over, Gary went into work feeling absolutely appalled at himself. He took off his shoes and socks and rolled up his trouser legs. Surely it was now just a matter of time. He lunched on red pepper, hot chillies, vinegar and lemon sauce, a beetroot and a bottle of Jamaican Bordeaux. For dessert he made himself eat a cigarette, though that he had to spit out.

When he got back home Judy gave him a lovestruck look as he entered. Annette said, 'Gary, I need to talk to you.'

She took him into the bedroom. 'I was just making the bed,' she said, and I found these.' She held up Judy's knickers. Annette had suspected Gary of having sex with some of the girls who had helped out with the kids in the past. Now at last she had proof.

'Aren't they yours?' Gary asked.

'No. They are not.'

'Wow, I wonder how they got in there.'

'You tell me, Gary. You tell me.'

On the phone to me later he said, 'Suddenly I did not want Annette to know – which was perfect. I was at last genuinely terrified of something. If she found out, she'd throw me out the house, she'd ban me from seeing the boys, and she'd take me for every single cent she could, as well as blacken my name to all our friends.'

'So what the hell did you tell her?' I asked.

'I said, "All right, Annette, I'll level with you. After you go to work, I sometimes wear women's underwear. I've been doing it for a few months now. I, you know, put it on to masturbate and then usually hide it or take it to the office. Today I was in a hurry and must have left it down the side of the bed."'

'Gary, these are Judy's.'

'I know, honey, but don't tell her, I beg you. I snuck in and stole a pair. You see, yours didn't fit. I'm sorry, I am ashamed of myself. Look, don't judge me too harshly. I'm sure I can break the habit . . . Maybe there's a group someplace . . .'

Annette put her arm round Gary's shoulders. 'Honey, why didn't you tell me about this? You know me, I don't mind . . .'

She leant forwards and ripped a paper tissue out of the box and handed it to him. He had thought it safest to cry. 'I'm sorry,' he sobbed, 'I should have mentioned it but I just thought, What if it stops you loving me?'

Annette knew that something had been worrying Gary. This was obviously why he'd been acting so weirdly. The poor guy had got really hung up on this tiny thing. Even Bud had rung her to say that he'd been acting strange at the office. She felt bad she had suspected him of having it off with Judy. 'Don't hate yourself,' she said comfortingly, 'it's nothing to be ashamed of.'

Three nights later and the skin was still silky and smooth. Not even a tiny red spot of guttate, or a loose scale or two around his ankle. What was his problem? Over in Miami, Tina said goodbye to her cat, Peder, and set forth for the airport to catch the American flight to Montego Bay.

As Gary was undressing for bed, Annette, lying under the sheet reading the sexy pages of Shere Hite said, 'Hey, your skin's so good. Maybe you are finally cured.'

As he pulled on his yellow silk pyjamas, Gary thought of Tina's nubile little body. He had often told me that her bikinis looked like a packet of triangular stamps. He got into bed. It had not been a good day – he had weakened and eaten a salad for lunch when he shouldn't have had anything less than two Big Macs with large fries. He was switching off his

light when Annette said, 'Hey, honey, I bought you something today.'

'Oh yeah, what?'

'These.' Annette took from her bedside drawer a pink lacy
set of knickers and bra for a fat woman with no bosoms. 'Why
don't you try them on?'

'Er, I don't think so . . .'

'Go on, Gary, don't be shy, it's okay.'

Gary decided that he had to try them on. It would look
too weird if he didn't. He got out of bed, dolefully removed
his pyjamas, folded them carefully on the chair. Annette threw
him the bra and panties. He pulled them on with a heavy
heart.

'Hey, you look great, Gary, they fit really well. Check yourself out in the mirror. Yeah, sexy . . .'

Gary looked in the mirror. He did not like what he saw,
especially the healthy skin on his shins. He turned Annette
on, who secretly had long held fantasies about Gary in women's
clothes. She made him have sex with her for hours.

'That was great, Gary – wow, isn't it amazing that we're still
discovering sexy things about each other after fifteen years of
marriage? Hey, honey, you wouldn't get me some apple juice
from the refrigerator, would you?'

Gary went out into the corridor. As he passed the *au pair*'s
room, the door opened. Judy had been lying on her bed waiting
for Gary to make his move. She wanted his baby.

'Hey, Gary, Gary, come here,' she whispered. 'I thought you
weren't coming.'

'Oh, hi Judy.'

'Come in . . .'

'No, I'm just getting juice for Annette.'

'After that, come to me. Say you're doing some work.'

'No, I can't.'

'I thought you loved me.'

'Okay, I'll be back in a minute.'

He looked in the fridge. He knew he should eat at least a hunk of Camembert, half a red pepper and swig at a bottle of stinking vinegarish Puerto Rican Burgundy, but his stomach rebelled at the thought. He hated this frigging diet. His hand hesitated over the Camembert and then moved down to the forbidden crisper. He just wanted a green salad and some lightly boiled organic vegetables with a glass of iced mineral water, that's all. He found a carrot in the crisper and ate it in chunks ravenously and sinfully. He closed the fridge door. He didn't want to go and shag Judy, so he tiptoed past her door.

'Gary,' she whispered. 'Gary!' But he kept on going back to his own room. This was going to end in divorce, not the Negril Beach Club. He went up the corridor to his own bedroom where Annette was now asleep. He lay down beside her and closed his eyes.

The next night he rang me to say he was calling off the campaign. That afternoon he'd driven over to see a producer in Malibu and nearly ran over the woman's son in her drive. He'd said, 'Whoops,' as he walked unevenly to the front door, and the producer had looked aghast. At that very moment, for the first time in a year, Gary felt a little flush of something nervy in his bloodstream, and a light stinging on his face and legs, which he recognised as a shot of psoriasis. But was this what it was going to take? Child murder? He was pushing the envelope too hard. Nothing, not even a month in 404 with Tina, was worth that.

He returned to the office, sobered up, called me, and quit the attempt to get psoriasis. He phoned Tina, who was already in 404, to say he wasn't going to make it that year. He resigned himself to not seeing his old and familiar friends in Jamaica, all of whom knew him as Tina's boyfriend and allowed him fully to indulge the fantasy of his second life on the shores of the Caribbean.

But when he got home that night he was surprised to find Annette standing in the dark hall in her dressing gown, her hair and make-up all messed up.

'Hi honey, you gave me a fright standing there in the dark like that.'

She reached out and took both his hands in hers. 'Are you okay, Gary, honey?'

'Yeah.'

'I been worried about you.'

'Well, I've been feeling a bit weird, but I'm better now. Whatever it was, I think is over.'

'I thought maybe you should see Dr Moynihan.'

'That won't be necessary.'

'Why don't you come with me tomorrow? I've got to go in because, well you'll never guess. I have psoriasis.' She opened the gown. 'I've been so stressed-out lately.'

Gary had a look at Annette's stomach. She had a light rash of guttate psoriasis, an archipelago of tiny red islands. After he switched the bedside light off he found her hand in bed. 'Don't worry, honey,' he said, 'you'll be okay, you'll see.'

'I think the last few weeks have been a bit of strain on me.'

'Yeah, I'm sorry,' said Gary, 'I've not been in good shape, I apologise . . .'

'Thanks,' she said. 'I guess the best thing is for me to go straight to the Negril Beach Club, maybe it can do for me what it did for you,' she said.

Gary's blood ran cold. Annette – at the Club? With Tina there? It could not be allowed to happen. All the staff thought he was married to Tina. It was just too dangerous. The thought of it shook his bones in their sockets, and that very night Gary's nervous system, supercharged by horrible dreams of detection, humiliation and expulsion from his beautiful big Westwood house and his lovely blond family, pushed the psoriasis into his every artery, vein and capillary, and by the morning, when he woke up, he felt his skin tingling with what he recognised as the beginnings of a major crash. By the following day he was full to the brim. His ankles and shins gave up their powdery harvest. A day later he found scales on the dressing room floor for the first time in a year.

Annette agreed that Gary had to get out to Jamaica fast. The strange thing, to her, was that his behaviour returned to normal. He once again seemed like his old relaxed self. This had a miraculous effect on her own skin. With the help of a tube of cortisone from Dr Moynihan, the little scabs on her tummy first faded, then disappeared, and on the day Gary left for the Negril Beach Club, Annette's skin was back to normal.

I've got something to tell you

I saw sex everywhere – or rather I didn't see anything that was not sex. And it was definitely getting worse. Food, architecture, animals, children, old people, serious books, newspapers, sport and the weather just dimmed and faded from my life. And anything that could be sexualised leapt out at me in full colour.

A typical quarter of an hour went like this: I'd drive into a garage to fill up. I picked up the nozzle, stared at it as it morphed into a penis. I removed the petrol cap. Stared at the hole. I placed the nozzle into the petrol tank. The glugging sound melted into sounds of sex. I replaced the nozzle and walked into the shop – everything was a grey sludge except for the row of pornographic magazines which blazed away on the top shelf. I looked at the queue, and was drawn to the longer one that had the pretty female cashier. I looked into her eyes and suddenly realised that this woman, whom I had never seen before, was the answer to the squirming knot of dread and pain in my stomach. We exchanged no words apart from, 'Would you like a VAT receipt?' 'No thanks,' but when I pocketed my wallet and walked back to the car I felt like Dr Zhivago leaving Lara.

A parking meter was a pulsating phallus, the credits on the TV programme *Countdown* became *Cuntdown*, and when I was in a post office and a woman said, 'Would you like this to go second class?' I heard 'Would you like to smell my ass?'

It became impossible to be with my friends. I hadn't seen Howard for years – what was the point? Even *I* drew the line at having sex with him. The same went for Claire – they were just losers stuck in skin hell. I was in post-psoriasis heaven. If I spent any time with siblings, or my mother, or my old friends, a voice in my head – was it psoriasis? – shouted, 'What are you talking to them for? You can't shag them. Stop wasting time.'

Initially Sexworld was one I could enter and leave, almost at will, but what had started as a merry adventure with me and my new skin turned dark. I had pushed through the fur coats in the wardrobe and entered a Narnia of sex, but now when I tried to find my way back I got lost, and when I did manage to stumble back through the wardrobe into the real world, unlike the children in the book I found that hours, days, weeks had passed in my absence.

I tried to drink it away, I tried to drug it away, but nothing worked. I was hurting inside, frightened, feeling totally out of control. Many times I decided to stop hunting for sex and return to the happy fold of my family, but I could never draw a line in the sand without stepping straight over it.

I had a favourite walk I used to take in the old days in times of trouble, usually when my skin was getting me down, up behind my house, high on to the deserted moor. There I could lie in the heather and soothe myself with the long view of the hills galloping away into the mists of Snowdonia. I dragged myself up there one autumn afternoon to find solace. Rays of sunlight fanned from a dark cloud. The oak woods below me were no doubt in their full damp glory – yellows, orange, browns and black – but I couldn't see any of the colours in the thirty-mile vista in front of me, nor could I pick out the contours of the hills or the outline of the trees: it had all turned into a huge grey mush. Its magnificence meant nothing to me any more.

In a walkers' car park four hundred yards below me I saw a car draw up, and a woman get out. She opened the back door to lean in to take a baby out of a child seat, revealing a band of flesh between her jeans and T-shirt. This little sliver of skin made more impression on me than all the vast beauty of the landscape.

I went back to the house, weary. I was aware by then just

how crazy making and abusive it was for my wife to be subjected to my bullshit. I passed her in the kitchen and smiled weakly. For ten years she had raised our children, supported me, helped me, encouraged me and loved me in her fine and brilliant manner. The weight of all that I had done pressed down on me. I went upstairs and lay on our bed, staring at the huge old beech tree whose limbs reached the window. I used to love its fat trunk and blazing colour, but hadn't noticed it for years.

A phrase came to me: what if I told the truth?

And a voice like rat poison said, 'Don't even think about it.' It was as clear as if it were in the room with me.

But I just wanted this awful mess to stop. I just wanted to surrender.

'No!' shrieked the voice. 'Don't! You can't! You must lie. You must!'

Five minutes later I went back down to the kitchen where my wife was lovingly arranging laundry on the rack. She always did it so carefully.

'I've got something to tell you,' I said.

Part 2

12

Males Only

I was being driven by an old man in a baseball cap along a desert road through a flat pale landscape dotted with desiccated bushes and soraya cacti to The Meadows, a rehab centre in Arizona. The prospect of a five-week stay didn't alarm me because I knew I would be amongst the kind of women I found so attractive – vulnerable women who were desperate for attention. My plan to launch into this easy prey was set back by a three-inch-square cardboard sign that. I was told to hang round my neck, which stated simply, 'MALES ONLY'. It meant that I was not permitted any conversation or any contact of any kind with women for the duration of my stay, which felt from the moment I hung it round my neck like it was going to be four years rather than four weeks. I couldn't sit at the same table with them in the canteen; I couldn't even say good morning when we passed in the corridors. There was one exception to the rule – Lola, a heavily tattooed lesbian with eyes that very clearly stated, Don't try any of your fuckin' funny stuff on me, you creep.

I thought that getting the MALES ONLY sign was the lowest point in my life, but I was wrong; that came a few hours later after I was conducted through a set of addiction indices. This entailed me sitting with a uniformed nurse in a small room off the main reception crisply and coolly answering hundreds of questions about my life. She started with alcohol.

'Do you ever say you won't drink, and then do?'

'No.'

'Do you feel anxious without a drink?'

'No.'

'Have you been twenty-four hours without a drink?'

'Yes.'

'Have you ever hidden your drinking?'

'No' . . . and many others along the same lines, none of which seemed hard to answer honestly.

She moved on to drugs: 'Have you ever lied about using drugs when you are on them?'

'No.'

'Do you have difficulty sleeping without drugs?'

'No.'

'Have you ever lied to a doctor to get a prescription?'

'No.' Etcetera.

And then on to gambling: 'Have you ever spent more than you planned gambling?'

'No.'

'Have you ever sold a personal item to get money to gamble?'

'No,' and so forth.

She progressed to spending and shopping: 'Have you ever bought an item of clothing and not worn it?'

'Yes.'

'Rarely?'

'Yes'

'Often?'

'No.'

'Habitually?'

'No.'

Food: 'Do you eat in secret?'

'No.'

'Have you ever made yourself vomit after eating?'

'No.'

And finally to the questions I feared.

'Do you think about sex at inappropriate moments?'

I thought about asking her the definition of inappropriate – a word I was to hear a lot at The Meadows – but thought, what the hell, I know the answer. 'Yes.'

'Have you ever bought pornography?'

'Yes.'

'Have you viewed pornography on the internet?'

'Yes.'

'Have you spent more time viewing pornography than you wanted to?'

'Yes.'

'Has your work suffered because of your sexual behaviour?' (I heard beaver.)

'Yes.'

'Has your family life suffered because of your sexual behaviour?'

'Yes.'

'Do you masturbate to go to sleep?'

'Yes.'

'Have you ever masturbated for more than one hour?'

'Yes.'

'Have you ever masturbated for more than four hours?'

I had been carefully avoiding looking at her, but that one made me look up in surprise. Four hours? You wouldn't have thought a man's wrist could take it, let alone his penis. 'No.'

She continued calmly: 'Has your spouse or partner ever voiced concern about your sexual behaviour?'

'You could say that,' I answered, hoping to get a smile.

She looked at me blankly. 'Is that a yes or a no?'

'Yes.'

She ended eventually with 'Have you ever attempted to commit suicide?'

No, but now you mention it, I thought.

'Do you have suicidal ideation?'

'What does that mean?'

'Have you ever visualised or planned suicide?'

'No.'

I waited while she totted up the scores.

'You will be in grey group,' she said.

'What does that mean?'

'Your sex index indicates you may be a sex addict. I want you to sign this. It's an abstinence contract.' She pushed a piece of paper towards me. It was an agreement not to masturbate during my stay. It was incredible how calmly and openly she broached this distasteful subject.

'But that's not what I'm here for,' I said, 'I mean . . .'

'It's part of the treatment. Please sign it. Here. And here.' Her short unvarnished nail pointed to the paper. I picked up the Biro.

To complete my humiliation she removed all my books, my tube of cortisone – goodbye old friend – and my razor.

'What am I going to shave with?'

'You may come to the nurses' station and sign it out every morning and sign it back in after you shave.'

'But why?'

'Self-harm.'

'But—'

'It's part of the treatment.'

Feelings Check

The Meadows theory of addiction was that an addict is some-body who has developed a skill at anaesthetising emotional pain with either a substance or a behaviour. The treatment comprised of finding the source of the emotional problem and learning new techniques to deal with it when it came up. Dopamine is the chemical released into the brain by cocaine that produces the high, and it is dopamine that floods the brain during sex. And it is dopamine that I was using to get me through life. The question was, why did I need it? And the search for the answer commenced in the small cork-lined room where the grey group met with Todd, our counsellor. Todd was a tall bearded grizzled man who quickly told us just how many addictions he had battled with and beaten. All the staff were ex-addicts and there seemed to be a quiet competition going on over exactly which one had been the worst before finding salvation in recovery. Jack, a jolly rotund man who was in charge of blue group, proudly claimed to have had his first pipe of crack when he was five.

Within thirty-six hours of ceasing any flirting, planning sex or indeed having any, I soon found out why I had got so reliant on these things. I felt absolutely 100 per cent shit. I burst into tears about twenty times a day, and when I wasn't blubbing I was shaking with panic. Sleep was a nightmare.

The regime was tough – there were none of the little things we all used to soothe ourselves – novels, magazines, newspapers, TV, films, music and most notably caffeine. But they took a liberal line on cigarettes and prescription drugs, which most patients were prescribed to deal with depression. I fought not to join the long line of patients who queued each day at the meds counter to get their tiny cardboard cup with a pill in it. The psychiatrist said I needed it – but it seemed to run counter to the rest of the programme, which was about facing the pain inside me. In the end I refused to take it. I didn't say that I thought they were wrong to hand out so many drugs in a rehab facility. I had quickly learnt that it wasn't a place where you made complaints. The staff appeared to love watching grown men tantruming about the rules, and doing nothing about it. Randal, a blue-blooded East Coast billionaire was constantly asking 'to see the management' as though we were in a hotel, to complain about the mattress, or the cleaning or the heating, or the lighting, or the washing facilities, all to no effect.

There was an institution called Feelings Check, which involved going to the nurses' station every six hours, except at night, to report what you were feeling. They held up a board that read:

FEAR
PAIN
SHAME
ANGER
PASSION
JOY
LOVE
GUILT

On my first visit I said, 'I feel fine, fine . . .' notwithstanding the tears that were pricking my eyes at the time, and the deep blush that had engulfed me when I had arrived.

'Fine is not a feeling,' said the nurse. 'You have to pick one at least off the board.'

'Fine stands for fucked-up, insecure, neurotic and emotional,' said Barney, my roommate. 'They told me that when I said it.' Barney was a short and tubby man, with apologetic eyes half hidden behind thick glasses. He wore soft loose elasticated sports trousers, new trainers and a baggy T-shirt that said 'BUM EQUIPMENT'. He told me he had 'issues around voyeurism and exhibitionism'. This was Barney's way of saying that when he wasn't crouching in bushes looking into ladies' bathrooms in his native Fort Worth, he was indulging his uncontrollable desire to strip off his clothes and run round a city block stark naked at four in the morning.

The idea behind the Feelings Check was that people who do not or cannot express their feelings create the kind of inner tension that requires anaesthetising. I realised that I had a lot of difficulty identifying my feelings, let alone articulating them, and the exercise with the Feelings board, which took place in the busy nurses' station, where everyone could hear you, opened my eyes to how bunged up I was emotionally. I don't believe I had ever actually said the sentences, 'I feel sad,' or, 'I feel pain,' or, 'I feel scared,' before in my life. I was always just fine. All Kennaways were fine. At all times. That was how it was in our family. Simply articulating my feelings to somebody who said nothing in return but, 'Thank you, Guy,' in a singsong southern accent turned out to be a huge relief.

Other parts of the programme were not so pleasant. In front of the group, I had to go back over my past and dig up all the painful and embarrassing things that I had stuck away, hoping they'd just disappear. In fact, most people in grey group had had a much more traumatic childhood than me. I was embarrassingly under-abused. There were two who had been abandoned as infants, one who'd seen his father shot, and another two who had been violated by clergymen. There were eight patients in total who had suffered at the hands of the church. All of them were taking legal action against their dioceses, which were also footing their rehab bills. I worked out that ten per cent of The Meadows' income was from the Roman Catholic Church.

I was encouraged to reassess my upbringing, and got the feeling – no, the *idea* – ('a thought is not a feeling, Guy') that Todd was desperate to pin something heinous on my mum or dad. It would have made the whole process easier if I'd had some kind of childhood trauma to hang my problems on. In the end Todd had to settle on telling me that my childhood was at times 'less than nurturing'.

'But that's enough,' Todd told me. 'If you feel pain about it, that's still pain.'

I could not tell, and do not know to this day, if I was hurt as a child by my parents. I can point to others who had a much rougher time than me who haven't been eaten up by it the way I was. It is certainly painful being me, and it occurred to me that psoriasis was at least one of the causes. Bad skin had made me scared to be myself; for years my default emotions were shame and pain on its account.

I certainly didn't have problems with sex before I had bad skin, in contrast to the others in grey group whose tortured histories all went back to their childhoods.

I became humourless and earnest in my quest for recovery. It's a sign of how desperate I was to have my life back that I was prepared to swap it for making jokes. But there were some guys who didn't take rehab seriously. It turned out that Randal was doing his fourteenth stint in eight years. He had to be there to satisfy some distant trustees who threatened to remove his massive fortune if he didn't sober up. Others were there because their lawyers said it would look good in court. These were DUIs; one man who was transparently only going through the motions was trying to convince a judge he had turned over a new leaf so he wouldn't lose custody of his kids.

The process was like moisturising a desiccated soul. In the lecture halls – where I always sat like the teacher's pet at the front taking notes – I was re-taught how to live. For a week I was made to wear a hula-hoop around me, to teach me that all of us have a circle of space which we are safe within and that nobody can enter without permission. It seemed idiotic at first, coming out of the rooms and filling my lungs with serene desert air, to be holding a ring of plastic around my waist – but these exercises were cunning, and within a few days I started feeling safer, because of the protection it offered me, than I had before.

Todd introduced me to the concept of co-dependence, a term which had been coined at The Meadows, and which is now widely, and often wrongly, used.

'Do you notice how reactive you are when you enter a room?' Todd asked.

'What do you mean?'

'You come into a room, and you look around to see who is in it and what kinds of moods they're in, before you act.'

'Mmm,' I thought about that. 'Maybe,' I said.

'You have a highly developed antenna for what you think people wish to hear.'

'That sounds terrible,' I said, 'but I know what you mean.'

'It's a coping mechanism, Guy. You developed it to protect yourself. It means that you're more interested in what other people are thinking of you than your own truth.'

'That's true,' I said, 'I'll say anything to avoid confrontation.'

'Sure, but of course you have no idea what is in other people's heads, and your attempts to please them . . . well, you tell me how successful you've been.'

'Not at all. Everybody's very angry with me.'

'You do not know that. What you know is that you have failed to be truthful to yourself.'

'To do that, I'd need to know who I am,' I smiled, 'which is not so simple in my case.'

'That's what you're here for,' he smiled. Then he leant back, and said, 'Good work.'

The process of finding out who I was started in the art room of all places. They always sent you there when the task was clearly far too big to deal with in any rational way. It was a messy space decorated with garish pictures entitled, 'ANGER', 'SHAME', 'MY DEAD BABY', 'DONNY', 'GOODBYE ADDICT!' and 'FUCK YOU, PA'. I stared at a bit of white paper while Randal, beside me, traced his picture of God, an image we were all told to produce, off a drawing.

'They always get you to do the image of God,' he told me, 'so I just carry this picture around with me.' He showed me the drawing he was copying. 'I picked it up at Promises, or was it Hazleton? Or Cottonwood. One of them. Some soppy girl did it. I like it. It always impresses the counsellors. Never fails.' He held up the drawing of a dove rising from a pair of hands at sunset. I got the impression Randal did not think this was the last time he'd need it.

I splashed paint around for session after session in the art room on my quest for my identity, but unearthed only one incontrovertible truth about myself: I am no painter.

Out of the Shadows

Dr Carnes, the great sex addiction guru, whose groundbreaking book *Out of the Shadows* brought the subject respectability in the States, gave a series of lectures. A tall, fit fifty-five-year-old, he spoke with burning certainty and energy, the St Paul of the religion of sex addiction, proselytising about it wherever and to whomever he could, and in so doing pushing it into public consciousness.

Although all addictions were treated basically the same at The Meadows there was clearly a hierarchy of addicts. At the top of the tree were the junkies, represented by Sally, a dark-haired, white-faced Goth who, though the daughter of a senator, lived on the streets of Los Angeles before being dragged to the ranch by her parents' Intervention Man – a craggy-faced, lean cowboy who was paid to bring fuck-ups into rehab by desperate friends and families, and who I occasionally glimpsed in reception with some hapless soul. Heroin addiction had such a noble tradition, from Thomas De Quincey, through Coleridge and Conan Doyle to William Burroughs and Kurt Cobain. It had history, it had breeding. It was unquestionably the premium addiction.

Alcoholism was the standard addiction – solid, dependable, popular and as effective at destroying lives as any other, and it was well represented at The Meadows. Gambling came next, with its spectacular ability to strip people of every possession they owned. Gerry, a Mafia member in grey group, who had gambling as well as sex, had a contract out on him after losing his gang's takings at a Las Vegas crap table. Food, spending and plastic surgery were new-wave addictions, still looking to make their mark in the field. But sex addiction was unquestionably the addiction of the future. Most of the sex addicts at The Meadows had already duelled with alcohol and/or drug addiction, and had come back into rehab to sort their sex addiction out, realising that it had triggered their drug and alcohol issues (as problems were called there). A quarter of the sixty patients at the ranch had sex problems, and the number had been steadily rising over the years. The advent of HIV had made sex addiction a more dangerous proposition than shopping, gambling or spending. It was a killer, so was moving up the league table of addictions, though it still lacked history and breeding. In most countries it wasn't even acknowledged as an addiction, and in some was considered a virtue.

Every evening the patients with sex issues were brought together in meetings to talk and listen to each other. The first night I went to one of these sessions, I found about twenty men sitting in a circle of chairs. Barney distributed boxes of Kleenex so there was a tissue at hand for us all. My God, I thought to myself, they're so out of control they even have to knock one off the wrist in a public meeting. But as the meeting got under way I discovered the Kleenex were for tears, nothing else.

Dr Carnes had a theory that the urge to behave addictively is stored deep in the subconscious brain, rather than in the more easily programmable front brain. This was why it was so difficult to alter my behaviour – even when I wanted to. It was in the wiring of the computer, rather than the software. To reprogramme the subconscious – he argued – we had to create unusual conditions, so that the information could penetrate the protective software, which the addiction, like a virus, had corrupted, to protect itself. Carl Jung had been the first psychoanalyst to tell an alcoholic patient that his only salvation lay in finding other drunks and swapping stories with them. Dr Carnes believed that Jung said this because way back in pre-history the only occasions that the early humans came together in formal groups were when something crucial was at stake, like a threatened attack on the community whether by an enemy or nature, events that required the community to dispense with messages from the front brain – all the superficial things like hunger, love and sex – to survive.

It was drummed into us that survival was at stake, and when we gathered together in our Fellowship groups, a weird kind of magic did descend on me, and I always emerged into the crisp desert air under the bright starry sky feeling more able to shift the way I lived.

Getting into groups and telling stories reminded me of the Dead Sea – where I had done the same thing during the long hours basting on the roof, and though none of it was formalised with the rituals of the Fellowship meeting, it too gave me the power to change who I was. Another similarity between the two places was their creation of a parallel culture. At the Dead Sea it was Uglyville, where to be normal looking was freaky. In the canteen at The Meadows you could talk and listen to conversations that would be unthinkable in the outside world. Groups of men sat round discussing shame, fear and pain with a dash of masturbation and crack addiction thrown in as if they were talking about the weather.

There was also a process of reducing our shame, which Dr Carnes said was only likely to make relapse into old behaviour more likely. He had designed an exercise to do this which involved telling the members of our core group our deepest darkest secrets, based on the premise that 'you are only as sick as your secrets' – one of the oft-quoted catchphrases of the place. Most of us unloaded dreadful seedy tales of atrocious sexual shenanigans, while the apparently unshockable Todd nodded and said, 'Good, okay . . . nice work,' as if we were admitting we'd once run a red light when there was no traffic around. The atmosphere in these sessions was so sacred and trusting that Gerry, the Mafioso, fessed up to killing three men, quickly changing the story to accidental deaths on building sites when Todd said he was duty-bound to report any criminal activity to the Federal Authorities. As I spilt out the dreadful details of my crazy sex life I felt my heart and soul lighten, and my resolve never to slip back into the gutter strengthen.

Colditz

As the place grew familiar and the faces more friendly, I started to appreciate the life of the cafeteria and the patient lounge. The majority of the patients were American, but the addition of a handful of English, Canadians, South Africans and Australians gave it the whiff of a World War Two prisoner-of-war camp movie. The inmates were all addicts who had bought it over enemy territory. Occasionally the gates would open and another man or woman would shuffle in, in pretty bad shape after a desperate time on the run, getting caught and roughed up by the authorities.

I used to speculate with Barney whether there was an escape committee overseeing breakout attempts. Were the bulimics burrowing under the wire to come up under the snacks aisle in the local supermarket? Did the alcoholics have one aimed for the liquor store? The sex addicts' tunnel would come up under a Santa Fe strip joint, and the depressives, led by heavily bearded Larry, who sat blank faced and silent at all meals, were tunnelling out to a desolate spot in the desert where they could climb out and feel comfortingly isolated.

As soon as I sat down in the cafeteria, people sidled up to me to ask the circumstances of my capture.

'Hi,' said a dishevelled, tired-looking man of about fifty whose tag indicated he was called Rob. 'Do you want that sugar?' He pointed with a shaking, nicotined finger at the rationed single sachet of sugar I had been given at the servery.

'No, I don't eat sugar.'

'You mind if I take it?'

'No,' I said. 'Go ahead.'

Rob's hand darted out and grabbed it. 'I crave sugar since detoxing the booze,' he said, slipping it into the pocket of his stained black trousers. 'Some of the eating disorder girls,' he continued, nodding towards a table of thin and fat women eating under the watchful eye of a nurse, 'will pay hard cash for sugar, but they don't really need it like me. You give it to them and they just vomit it up. It's a waste. What are you here for?'

'Sex,' I muttered into his food.

'I'm here for the old juice,' Rob said.

'Do you think it's good here? I mean, does it work?' I asked, hoping for encouragement.

'This place? I doubt it. What can they do in five weeks, when we've spent a lifetime getting addicted? I mean, what chance is there of getting cured? Very, very little. Excuse me.' He went to the next table, where he said, 'You using that sugar?'

Gerry sat down beside me. 'He was a bit depressing,' I said.

'Dontcha listen to Wob, Guy. He's got a weal down on this place. He wants to welapse, that guy, that's how I see it. He wants to. And if you enter with that attitude, well, what chance is there?' We ate in silence as the idea of wanting to relapse hung in the air between us. Gerry then said, 'Sometimes I get weal scared about the way I might want to go back to my old ways once I'm outa this place. Here it's okay, I can hold it together, but what if I get out and welapse? I can't do that stuff no more. I'm pwaying this pwogwamme works, you know? Because I can't do that stuff no more.' We fell silent again. 'Wob take your sugar?'

'Yes,' I said.

'He uses it to make the love and food addict girls flirt with him. Well, they fall in love easy for a bag of sugar, don't they? And Wob don't have to wear no males only badge.'

Love addiction was one of the new conditions that I had learnt about. Love addicts lived for that intoxicating feeling people get when they meet someone special and start falling in love – except that with love addicts the word 'special' can be removed from the above sentence. They were able to whip up the euphoria of falling in love with almost anyone they met. They could make avowals of lifelong devotion thrice daily, if necessary. And they cared as much about the person they were falling in love with as an alcoholic cares about the vintage of the wine he's drinking, or the sex addict cares about the person he's having sex with.

'You're going to make it, Gerry,' I said. 'Then you'll only have to worry about being killed by the Mafia.'

He looked at me. 'Don't even fugging joke about it, Guy,' he said. Then he put his huge hand on my arm. 'But you can make it too, you know? You can make it. I believe in you. I do. You are not evil, you're not bad; you're sick, and you can get better, you can make it.'

'Thanks Gerry,' I said.

Walking from the cafeteria back to my room I passed the nurses' station.

'Feelings Check, Guy,' one called out to me, holding up the board:

FEAR
PAIN
SHAME
ANGER
PASSION
JOY
LOVE
GUILT

I had chosen guilt and shame and pain so often, I nearly did the same without thinking.

'Take your time,' the nurse said.

I breathed deeply and tried to untangle the knot of emotions inside my body. Then I said, 'You know, I think I feel joy. Yes, I do. And passion.'

'Okay, joy and passion,' she said, ticking my chart. 'Thank you.'

Disclosure

Week four was Family Week. This was traditionally the time when the parents turned up to get both barrels from their offspring. I watched Barney confront his huge redneck dad about the beatings he had received with a studded belt all through his childhood – apparently to ensure that Barney didn't grow up to be a homosexual. Dad refused to give ground.

'Well it worked, didn't it?' he said. 'Or don't tell me you're one of those as well as this . . .'

But Todd ground him down, as he did every parent who came into the sessions, and after a few hours Dad did concede that, 'Well, heck, I guess I may have been a little hard on you, son.' At which Barney burst into tears and the two of them hugged while we applauded.

I didn't want to invite my mother, but Todd said, as he always did before he made me do something horribly painful, 'Just trust the programme, Guy.'

My mother didn't come. She was too ill to make the trip. It probably looked to her like a process which she was not going to be able to control. For decades her technique of dealing with painful episodes was simply to deny their existence. This was not The Meadows' *modus operandi*. In the end I had to do what is termed 'empty chair work' which meant I got to beef about my childhood to a plastic stackable seat, imagining my mother to be perched on it listening attentively in silence to my list of grievances – an unlikely event had she actually been there.

A good friend sent me a Shakespeare sonnet. The bard, of course, with the secret of life in his hands, knew all about sex addiction:

Th'expense of spirit in a waste of shame
Is lust in action; and till action, lust
Is perjured, murd'rous, bloody, full of blame,
Savage, extreme, rude, cruel, not to trust,
Enjoyed no sooner but despisèd straight,

Past reason hunted, and no sooner had
Past reason hated as a swallowed bait
On purpose laid to make the taker mad;
Mad in pursuit and in possession so,
Had, having, and in quest to have, extreme;
A bliss in proof and proved, a very woe;
Before, a joy proposed; behind, a dream.
All this the world well knows, yet none knows well
To shun the heaven that leads men to this hell.

Too intelligent

In Spirituality Week I got to paint my picture of God. Randal sweetly offered me his hands, dove and sunset to copy. I declined on grounds of kitschness, but I was definitely going to need some kind of crib. I looked at the blank paper and considered the problem. The problem was simple. I didn't believe in God. Todd, and many others, had explained to me that to get myself sorted out I was going to have to find a 'higher power' to believe in.

'I'm not sure I can do that,' I told him.

'Now why doesn't that surprise me?' Todd said.

'I'm too intelligent to do something as simple as that,' I said. He just smiled.

'You know, Guy,' he said, 'you do believe in God.'

'Please, Todd, spare me the crap,' I said.

'You do,' he said, 'and you know who your God is?'

'Tell me,' I said with a bored sigh.

'You. You think you make all the rules and are all-powerful. It's true, isn't it? You can't even conceive of someone more powerful than you.'

I mulled over that gem for a few days. I had been brought up in Christian schools, and now believed churches to be little more than low-wattage magnets for third-rate minds, some of whom aspired to be clergy, though for that you had to be fourth-rate. And this wasn't even mentioning the frizzy hair, over-hemmed trousers, pale shoes, thin nylon socks and cheap anoraks that marked Christians out from the rest of the population. Nothing would get me back into a Christian church.

The alternatives were grim. Buddhism. Becoming a Buddhist seemed too voguish. The guys in the local pub would give me hell if I told them I was a Buddhist. The idea of becoming a Muslim was ridiculous for a middle-class man living in rural Wales. Hinduism, Jainism, Sikhism and Rastafarianism were also simply impractical. What else was there? However much I may have wanted to be religious it really wasn't possible. Did I really need the help of a god, the way Todd et al claimed? How could any deity be any more powerful than the person who believed in it? The buck stopped with me.

My urge to read had returned to me, though it could only be sated by 'recovery literature', the only texts permitted in the place. I learnt the sonnet that had been faxed to me, because I could now read poetry. I hadn't been able to read poetry for at least three years. On the occasions I'd tried, I'd got bogged down in the syntax or stalled in a pothole of a word whose meaning I once knew but had forgotten. But now I could read the sublime lines smoothly through from the first to the last. Four weeks earlier I had hardly been able to read a tabloid headline without resting halfway through. It was as if my hard drive, which had been stuffed full with rubbish and sex, had been cleaned, leaving space for less destructive information.

Deeply superficial

I was wandering around the car park late at night mumbling, 'I am enough, I have enough, I am enough, I have enough, I am enough,' over and over again, doing my affirmations; these were short phrases we were instructed to repeat time and again to try to get their message home. Cheesy, but if they worked I didn't care.

With my mind now clearer I was beginning to realise the enormity of what I had done, and the vastness of the task ahead of me if I wasn't going to do it again. I had gone outside under the stars with the vague hope that the clichéd setting of the desert sky might aid my search for God, which Todd was now hassling me about at every session.

There were one or two sun-faded cars in the car park, and I thought I'd take a quick look at the face in a wing mirror while I was waiting for the sweet Lord to do his work. There seemed to be nothing else to do. But as my reflection came into view and I started to focus on my epidermis it struck me just how superficial I was being. Deeply superficial, if that's possible, or unfathomably shallow. My surface – how I looked, how I appeared – was still everything to me. I stared into my eyes – I was going to have to look a little bit deeper than four layers of skin if I was going to change. My values were shit: I wanted to have integrity, and live in truth and honesty and openness, but here I was checking out my complexion again, hoping that if I looked okay I might fool someone that I was. My psoriasis had drawn me back on to its agenda. And I knew that for years I had been fretting over my skin when all the time it was *me* that was dry and flaky.

I looked up at a sodium light over the entrance to the car

park, and watched a pick-up truck head east down the lonely straight road towards Phoenix.

I knew what I had to do – I just didn't want to do it.

'Ah, fuck it,' I finally said to the compact Ford. 'Have it your way, Todd, I'll fucking believe in him if I have to. If it's going to get me out of this shit.'

And thus I got God.

13

De Gustibus Nil Disputandum

There is no standard of taste

Back in the real world, I had a lot of catching up to do, and started re-reading some old philosophy textbooks from university to get my brain working again. I came across an essay by the eighteenth-century sceptic David Hume, in which he stated that there were no absolute standards of taste – that everything to do with aesthetics was simply a matter of opinion. There never was and there never will be a single person or object that we all agree to be beautiful. Fairly obvious, but what if I was to substitute the word skin for the word object? Was finding a psoriatic skin ugly a mere opinion? Or was it just plain ugly? Full stop.

The ginger minger is a modern creation; when I was young in the 1960s no stigma was attached to having red hair. Quite the reverse: I remember my dad extolling Rita Hayworth's fiery locks, though it must be said he was more of a bulk consumer of women than a connoisseur. Something changed for redheads to cast them into ugliness. Can it all have been the work of the Duchess of York?

And something changed for bald men to catapult them out of ugliness (Yul Brynner aside). Pattern baldness has lost the stigma it carried in the seventies and eighties. I regularly see men with thinning hair on adverts, something unthinkable in baldness-free seventies TV land. In Jamaican culture there has never been a stigma attached to pattern baldness. They don't even have a word for it. 'Baldead' means short hair whether fashioned by a barber or nature. You may say that hair type or colour is not in the same category as skin texture, but in Jamaica I came across a more formidable Western stigma that they ignore: penis size. Nobody thinks it's important. In over twenty years of visits to the island I have never heard a taunt, or joke, about the size of a man's member. The only rapper to mention it is Eminem.

So why can't psoriasis be beautiful? Maybe its day will come. But perhaps not quite yet.

The first World Psoriasis Day fell on 24th October, 2004. Yes, I missed it as well. To coincide with it a survey was undertaken to establish people's attitudes to our disease. Its conclusions were headed 'People with Psoriasis Continue to Be Rejected by Others'.

It led for calls from a leading patient advocate, Lars Ettarp, President of the International Federation of Psoriasis Associations (IFPA), to 'ask for increased awareness, understanding and support for the disease'. It was a request that I think went mainly unnoticed. 'The five-country general-public study revealed that around half of all people would not kiss, hug, swim with or eat food prepared by someone with psoriasis' despite knowing that it was not contagious. 'The independent telephone survey of over five thousand demographically representative individuals revealed that less than one-third of respondents knew that psoriasis was a common disorder affecting one in fifty people' – most people thought that psoriasis was a much rarer skin disease with half thinking it affected one in a thousand or rarer (up to one in a million). Around three-quarters of people knew that psoriasis was a skin disease, but fourteen per cent thought that it was contagious. A fifth of those surveyed thought poor hygiene was the root cause of psoriasis.

There were some interesting differences between the results from different countries – for instance only thirty-eight per cent of Italians would kiss or hug a person with psoriasis compared to sixty-seven per cent of British respondents. Good old Brits, leading the way to our acceptance. Or is it just that they'll snog anyone?

The optimism of the report is almost tear-inducing for a psoriatic:

World Psoriasis Day, an initiative involving psoriasis patient associations across the globe, dermatologists and patients, marks a global 'wake-up' call to the misery and social exclusion of psoriasis and the launch of a new patient proclamation calling for urgent action to significantly enhance the quality of life of people with psoriasis . . .

'For the 125 million people worldwide who suffer from psoriasis, life can be extremely difficult and we are still discriminated against due to the unsightly appearance of our skin,' says Lars Ettarp from IFPA. 'We want a better standard of care for people with psoriasis. In short, we want hope for a brighter future.'

Prior to the last century, people with psoriasis had little choice of treatment to control their psoriasis. Because the skin disease was poorly understood and thought to be contagious, psoriasis sufferers were shunned and even confined to leper colonies.

(The survey was carried out by Taylor Nelson Sofres. World Psoriasis Day is sponsored by an unrestricted grant from Merck Serono.)

Not withstanding Lars's clarion call, I have yet to see a positive depiction of any skin disorder. We are still utterly marginalised. The National Portrait Gallery – that survey of British complexions over the centuries – has not a single plaque of psoriasis on its walls. It's hard to find any painter who has thought about rendering it, anywhere. Lucian Freud, known for his unflinching truthfulness when it comes to skin, has failed to paint it. He must either be paint-brushing it out, or deliberately choosing models without it.

In a survey of three magazines I carried out on the week of 8th January, 2007, I made the following discoveries.

Vogue had 354 images of faces, including its writers, photographers and contributors. I counted one beauty spot (an intriguing conceit) and a pair of gold spots painted on a girl's face. Otherwise every single face was apparently blemishless. *Vogue* does for complexions what Mills & Boon do for relationships. People would be up in arms if there were no black faces amongst that 354 – well, there were six: maybe they should be up in arms.

Horse and Hound featured forty-nine faces – not one with a spot or psoriasis, though I was pleased to see some impressively florid complexions under the riding hats in the hunting reports. There were horses with hides of many hues and patterns, photographed to display and celebrate their variety.

Grazia: 221 faces. Not one zit, not one plaque, not one birthmark. There was a full-page advert for 'Beautiful Clear Skin'. I also came across an article about a woman who bleached her black skin to be paler. And in *Now* magazine, which wasn't in my survey, I came across this letter:

> My mother's making my life hell. I'm nearly twenty and still haven't had a boyfriend yet. That's because I have had psoriasis since I was thirteen and I have a big birthmark on my right arm. And my chest is only an A-cup! To make matters worse, my father and I aren't close and my mother treats me like a slave and a prisoner. So how can I get a boyfriend?

Now's advice was:

> You really need to talk this through with both your doctor and a friend or counsellor: your GP can recommend one. I am sure that your skin problems can be helped or masked and you can learn to love your bosom the way it is.

So why can't she learn to love her skin, like her bosom, *the way it is*? By not giving this advice the agony aunt almost certainly made the psoriasis worse. People say that men with thinning hair help it fall out by constantly checking at it with tugs. Thus psoriasis feeds on itself; the worse we think it is, the worse it gets, the worse it *is*.

The beauty business

The offices of the internet newspaper *The First Post* have a security set-up that would be the envy of the Pentagon. I went there one spring afternoon to talk to the art directors about skin tones and textures in the media. I was signed in, given a badge, escorted to the lift, and dispatched to an upper floor where I waited in a leather armchair for Jenny and Tom, who appeared through a door that needed a swipe of a card to open again. We sat in a glass meeting room with a view of Kensington from six floors up in one direction and a silent newsroom of journalists staring at screens in the other.

We talked generally about the portrayal of beauty in the media – skinny models, black models, that kind of thing, and then I moved the conversation on to skin texture, and the depiction of skin in the media. I had noticed that Jenny had a couple of conspicuous raised moles on her face, and I thought she was a little uneasy about discussing skin.

I asked if it was part of their job to choose the photographs on the site. They said it was; it had been something they'd done for years on many magazines and newspapers, and both were experts on Photoshop, the software that allows the user to manipulate images.

'Tell me about the guiding principles of doctoring images of skin,' I asked.

'You can't be dishonest,' Jenny said.

'Like film posters, they Photoshop them too much, way past the point of honesty,' Tom said. He had clear pale skin, but like most people, he told me he had a friend who had struggled with psoriasis for years.

'So what kinds of things are we talking about?' I asked.

'Teeth whitening, eye whitening. Acne. When I worked on a teen magazine we got a photo from a prize-winner with really rough acne, and me and the production guy agreed we'd lessen it a bit. Not zit them all out. So it was still like her. That kind of thing goes on all the time. On *Vogue* we certainly got rid of moles.'

'What about Cindy Crawford's?' I asked.

'You don't touch that, it's an integral part of her face.'

'Is it the same with male faces?'

'No,' said Jenny, 'men can get away with a pitted complexion. It's rugged, isn't it? But not for a woman.'

'So where is the pressure to change the skin coming from? The editor? The circulation manager?'

They looked a bit sheepish.

'It's a well known fact,' said Jenny, 'that girl photo editors pick more pretty girls than men.'

'Does the character of the person affect the way their skin is treated?' I asked.

'It was hard to know what to do with the Ukrainian president whose face got messed up by poisoning,' Tom said.

'Viktor Yushchenko,' I said. 'An unquestionably good guy with unquestionably bad skin,' I said.

'That's him.' said Tom.

'Did you clean him up?' I asked.

'We couldn't, his face was the story, but he really stood out. It was hard to look at that photo.'

'Would it have been different if he wasn't so heroic?' I asked.

'Yes. You're less likely to clean up a bad man,' Tom said.

I later checked this theory by examining photos of Ian Huntley, the Soham murderer. Nobody had used the 'healing brush' on the dark rings of guilt and fear around his eyes, but then at least nobody had Photoshopped a dose of psoriasis on him, just to add to his evilness.

As I left, Tom laughed and said, 'We don't want to be blamed for this.'

I met photographer Scott Douglas for a demonstration of Photoshop. A friendly professional Glaswegian, Scott flipped open his laptop and brought up a photo of an actress with black skin. With a few clicks of the mouse he filled the screen with a square centimetre of her cheek, with its bumps and lines, and then magnified it again so they became trenches, craters and hummocks. Then with the cursor he started to flatten the contours.

'For a magazine cover they can spend sixty hours working on a single image,' he said, 'removing every flaw.'

'Have they always done it?' I asked.

'There wasn't so much manipulation, but now it's financially so accessible. It's a trend driven by technology, and driven by advertisers who rely on celebrity endorsement and the beauty business, where the celebrity becomes the brand and the person becomes unimportant.'

'They have the perfect skin,' I said, 'and it's the photographer's job to attach it to the model.'

'It's what sells the magazine,' he stated. 'I'll show you. Here's an example of someone who has particularly bad skin – but you wouldn't know it.' An image of a handsome grey-haired fifty-year-old man flicked on to the screen. 'If I do this,' Scott clicked an icon . . .

The man aged ten years in a millisecond.

'That's how it was before I cleaned him up. You can see his lips are aging. I just filled them out a bit.'

'Who is he?'

'An actor, it's for casting agents.'

'Did he ask you to clean him up?'

Scott smiled. 'No. They don't need to. They all want it. Everybody wants it.'

I sighed. 'What happened to "Beauty is truth, truth beauty – that is all/ Ye know on earth, and all ye need to know"?' I asked.

'People have expectations,' Scott said. 'All I am doing is matching expectations. The actor loved the shots. Skill with image manipulation makes a good photographer.'

With us sufferers hiding our psoriasis, and the media denying its very existence, the disease remains hidden, where it thrives. After my stay at The Meadows I began the adventure of meeting who was inside my skin. I forgave myself for not being so bloody perfect, and even got to like myself, however I looked, and whoever I was. Deep inside I felt the power of psoriasis loosen, but I still didn't quite find the courage to run my hands over my face, feel the ridges and flakes – yes, I am afraid they returned – and think, This is how God made me, this is who I am. It's okay.

When I saw a psoriatic on the street or in a pub I felt I knew all their cares and troubles and the shit they've been through and the shit they've been told and sold about their skin. Like the men and women in my addiction recovery group, we skin people were a band of comrades, and I was proud to be a member.

But I still couldn't be out about my skin. I still had my emergency tube of cortisone, I still had my high-collared shirts, my anti-dandruff shampoo, and my little strategies for hiding it when it got bad.

I was perturbed, no, angry, that we skin people are still seen as freaky, even though my face is more natural than any of the images on the cover of magazines. When psoriasis is excluded from the world, it makes me feel uglier, and I know this exacerbates the condition. The inability of smooth-skinned people to allow the existence of psoriasis, and embrace it, gives the illness to us. *I* have the symptoms of *their* disease.

14

Glory Be to God for Dappled Things

Howard's drinking buddy

Howard continued his treatment of his psoriasis systemically, not with methotrexate but with alcohol, in increasingly heavier doses. I looked him up and met him again, always in the pub, where he drank on his own, and gazed at me with eyes that had lost all their old mischief. He was a Caliban without the poetry. His stare was slow and glassy, as though he had left some crucial part of himself in the river the night he'd tried to kill himself. His clothes were dirty, his hair scurfy, his knuckles festooned with carbuncles of dead skin.

I told him about the Dead Sea and urged him to go, but he looked at me as if I were an idiot.

'It's really fantastic,' I enthused, 'you get such a sense of freedom there. It's like you shed your skin. The stuff comes back – sure – but for the months before it does you feel like you're flying. I think it'd be so good for you.'

He looked at me through gummy red eyes, paused and then said, 'Fuck off. You sound like some sodding evangelical preacher.'

He stood up, trudged over to the bar and returned with

two beers. I already had a drink, but he placed both glasses in front of him. The second pint, I realised, was for his psoriasis, his old chum, his drinking buddy, his companion through thick and thin, the only friend whom he hadn't pushed away, the way he was trying to push me away.

Salmon skin, lichen, leaves and feathers

I hadn't seen or spoken to Claire for a couple of years when she rang out of the blue.

'Come and have lunch,' she said, 'there's someone special coming. We've found Robert's son, he's called Tim, and we're going to meet him for the first time. I need someone to help us all relax.'

She welcomed me with a tight hug at the door of her home, a farmhouse of honey-coloured stone with a garden that ran down to a river grazed by a contented herd of Friesians on the far bank. I was surprised to see how untended her face was. Usually, before opening our front doors to guests, we carry out the necessary spot repairs, but Claire seemed oblivious of peelings around her hairline and mouth.

'Thanks for coming,' she said.

She closed the front door and led me through a wide hall that smelt of wood smoke and fresh flowers. I saw a book-lined study off it. 'How's your skin?' she asked, in the manner of veteran psoriatics.

'So so,' I said, 'How about you?'

'Ah, I don't worry about it any more.'

'Why not?' I asked, but she didn't answer.

We went into a kitchen warmed by a cream Aga. On the

sideboard were sliding piles of newspapers and on the dresser invitations and photographs. I watched Claire cup a fresh salmon in both her hands and curl its tail before carefully lowering it into a copper fish-kettle.

'Robert caught this on the last day of the season in Scotland. I don't want to harm its skin, doesn't it look lovely?'

'Magnificent,' I said, admiring its silver and greys, and smelling the river on its slimy surface.

'I think he's asked me to cook it so he can show it off to Tim,' she said, as she rinsed her hands. 'You know how to poach salmon, do you, Guy?' she asked, and then proceeded to inform me in her inoffensively bossy manner. 'Place it in cold water, bring it to the boil and then turn off the heat and let it cook in the water as it cools. It's the only way to make the flesh opaque and flaky, whatever weight the salmon.'

Claire took the top off a little pan and showed its contents to me. Sliced carrot sat on top of some grains of rice in water.

'That's what I'm getting,' she said.

'You still think that the answer is diet?' I asked her.

'I don't know. I suppose I'm so used to being on one I can't get out of the habit. Sometimes I believe that using diet to cure psoriasis is like thinking you can stop a car rusting by using a different brand of petrol.'

'Where's your husband?' I asked.

'Robert's somewhere outside, doing what he often does when he feels tense: roaming around the farm looking for trespassers to get annoyed about seeing.'

Later, he came through the back door with a bit more commotion than was necessary and entered the kitchen. He too was tall, and was well fed with a big hooked nose and thinning brown hair. We shook hands, and he launched into a tirade against a new bicycle path the County Council had built on the bed of the disused railway that ran through the property. He had run a campaign against it, but had failed to keep the bicyclists off their land. He started emptying his pockets of dirty old litter. 'Look what I picked up,' he said.

'Robert is obsessed by litter,' Claire said.

'I cannot stand seeing it, that's all. People who drop it should be banned from the countryside.' As he emptied his coat pocket of crisp packets ('called Walkers because walkers bloody drop them') and flattened cans, he spoke about the new cycle path. 'You know you can get bike trailers now. Have you seen them? Long-distance bicyclists pull them behind them. The Dutch love them. Someone could easily ride out from Swindon, it's only fourteen miles, rob our house and get away with their bicycle trailer stuffed full of our valuables.'

Claire was amongst the cool slate shelves of the larder looking for cream. I thought it was easiest to agree with him and said, 'Yes, definitely. That's a real problem, Robert.'

'There's no cream,' she called out. 'Bugger.' When she came back to the kitchen saying '. . . and I haven't got time to go and get any . . .' Robert was standing holding two bottles of wine.

'Something special or something nice?' he asked.

'What do you think?' she replied.

'I think we'll have this,' he selected the cheaper of the two bottles.

The sun appeared luminously through the mist and fleetingly

flooded on to the boards of the kitchen floor. 'Ah, some sun. Let me show you the garden,' Claire said to me.

Two Springer spaniels roused themselves from their bed when they heard the click of the door latch, and trotted along behind us as we walked the gravel paths of the garden.

'It suddenly occurred to me, after all these years, that I don't really mind my psoriasis.'

'But don't you feel ugly?' I asked.

'Only sometimes, when I weaken. Look, who said it's ugly? I mean, it's only variegated skin, isn't it? We love variegated ivy and geraniums, don't we? Or at least some people do. Psoriasis is perfectly natural, like the skin of that salmon or the peeling bark of a silver birch tree – nobody ever said they were abnormal. Nobody ever said they were ugly. In fact they're beautiful. There's a poem about it I learnt at school. I'm a Cheltenham Ladies' College girl. We had to do things like memorise poems. The poem is about how divine psoriasis, neuro dermatitis, vitiligo and acne are.'

She closed her eyes for a moment, and started:

Glory be to God for dappled things,
For skies as dada dada as a wounded cow,
Not wounded, bugger, what's the bloody cow? How does
   it go on?
For rose-moles in all stipple, upon something that swims;
Something, something chestnut falls; finches' wings;
Landscape plotted and . . .

'. . . oh bugger I can't remember it now, but it's so good. It's a list of beautiful things with spots, like us. You'd love it. I used to know both verses. If I stop thinking about it, it'll come back.'

I glimpsed the red plaques of psoriasis on the back of her knees in the little gap that appeared between her tweed skirt and wellington boots when she bent down to stroke the dog. Under wispy hair, the spaniel's tummy was covered in liver-coloured spots.

At one o'clock we were back in the kitchen waiting for Tim. Robert was peering out the leaded windows down the drive. 'Do you think a taxi from Swindon will find us?' he asked quietly. At that moment, over a stile at the bottom of the garden, with his bike on his shoulder, hopped a tall man wearing a corduroy jacket and black trousers.

'Who the blazes is that?' Robert exploded. 'He's actually coming to the house. The cheek of it.'

'It's Tim,' said Claire, recognising her husband in the stranger. 'Come on, let's meet him.'

Tim was quiet, polite, tall, a little stooped with hair thinning to a bald spot. His handshake was not perhaps as strong as Robert would have liked, but he seemed to make a favourable impression with his earnest, shy manner. At lunch he drank his wine quickly out of nervousness. He had a keen disinterest in financial matters, and talked knowledgeably and sensitively about food and wine, and a bit about art and architecture. His tastes were conservative. Claire served her rice and carrots for herself but ended up eating a hunk of poached salmon. She poured some wine and drank it. Her expression clearly told me that it tasted good after so long. The combination of the fish and the wine appeared at that moment to be well worth having psoriasis for. 'Bugger diets,' she said quietly to me as she refilled her glass. Robert was telling Tim about catching the salmon.

'I've had enough of diets,' she continued to me, 'my skin is my skin, it looks like it does. If people follow me around the supermarket staring at me when my face is all peely, it's their problem, not mine.'

After the tart, Claire served Jamaican coffee, which I noticed brought up a little patch of red skin beside her right nostril and another along her nose.

Tim wrote obituaries for a national newspaper. When Robert said, 'Oh, which one?' Tim pointed to the *Sunday Telegraph*, which lay on the ash bench beneath the window.

'Excellent, very good,' Robert said. 'Often the best page in the paper.'

'Thank you,' said Tim modestly. But he glowed with pleasure.

I hadn't had time to read the obituaries page. I had glanced at the results on the sports page to check Ipswich, thinking about Howard, but that was all. Robert poured the remains of the wine into Claire's glass and went to the cupboard to get out the better bottle.

'I think you might appreciate this,' Robert said, filling his son's glass.

After lunch the mist came rolling lazily back over the water meadows in giant wispy waves. Robert said, 'Shall we go for a walk? I'll show you a bit of the place. Tour the policies.'

'Can I borrow some boots?' Tim asked.

'What size are your feet?'

'Ten and a half.'

'Same size as me. Here.'

How these things were genetic. I remember Claire in a depressed moment telling me that the good thing about not having any children with Robert was that her psoriasis gene would be wiped out. 'So when I die, I will finally vanquish it,' she had told me with an untrue smile.

We walked up the drive over a hollow-sounding wooden bridge. Underneath, the river swam hard. A bicyclist went by on the lane and Robert flinched. There was nobody on the new bike path. I let the three of them go on ahead together.

I was horrified to see Tim take a packet of cigarettes from his corduroy jacket and peel off the cellophane. Claire too noticed and I knew she'd be praying he wouldn't drop it. He held the transparent packaging in his hand. Robert surreptitiously watched him. Cellophane was in a category, along with cigarette butts, the triangular corner of chocolate wrappers and the rind that sealed the top of plastic bottles, that Robert had told me annoyed him more than any other litter because people felt there was some excuse for dropping them. The same people, he had continued, twisted litter up to make it look as small as possible. Tim put the cellophane back in his pocket and lit a cigarette, throwing the dead match into the hedge. They turned off the lane at a stile and walked down a footpath. Ahead of them a half-inside-out Crunchie bar wrapper, with its characteristic silver lining, lay in the pale sand and gravel soil. Tim bent down to pick it up and put it in his pocket without saying anything. He saw Robert looking at him. 'Sorry, it's a habit of mine,' Tim said, 'I abhor litter.' I watched the relief and surprise in Claire's body.

Back at the house, the four of us had tea. The wine, food and emotional tension had taken their toll on Claire's face. It was puffy and red with lots of new peelings since Tim had arrived. I loved the way she didn't disappear to carry out any repairs or brush the flakes off her cardigan. She made eye contact with us all, boldly, unruffled by the colours on her face. She was so happy to have her husband's child in the house, to be able to be part of this unexpected scene, to be a mother. It was only natural that she wanted Tim to like her, but she had decided that her face was not something she was going to hide. The way she sat forward, with the light from the window full on her face, and laughed with Tim, touching him twice on the knee to get his attention, was so beautiful to see. All of her longing to have a family was given happy expression in the way she proudly produced a pot of tea and a fruitcake on a big tray, and said, smilingly, 'Well! Shall I be mother?'

When later they said goodbye to Tim outside the dark front door, Robert asked him to come again, in four weeks, and Tim said he wanted to do that. He then biked off, and Claire smiled to see Robert waving warmly at a cyclist. They turned back to the porch. Claire said, 'That was rather fun.'

Robert put his arm round her. 'He wasn't bad, was he?'

'No, he was very nice. A really nice man,' Claire said.

I went to ring for a taxi, but the number my driver had given me was engaged. As I came back into the hall I heard Robert say to Claire, 'I am so happy to have done that. I have been worrying about meeting him for thirty years. But he was a nice man, it went fine, I liked him. Thank you so much for being here. I could tell he liked you. Thank you, for every-thing. For everything. I really appreciate it.'

When we had put the last things in the dishwasher and Claire had scrubbed the fish-kettle she said, 'I think I might walk to church.'

My taxi number was still engaged. Claire said, 'Walk with me and I'll show you where you can get a taxi in the village. There's a little man there.'

We took the path across flat country towards the spire.

On the way through a wood, leaves were dropping as softly as big slow snowflakes. The first frost of the year had started the fall. Silver birches had bunches of yellow leaves amongst the green. In the disused canal, reeds and bulrushes stood in the still black water. Beyond, the oaks were changing colour. Claire said she had not seen many acorns that season. We stood at a gate and stared silently into a little field too boggy to have been of use to a farmer and whose hedges had been allowed to grow unclipped. Pale grey lichen flourished on the gate-post. The field's irregular shape spoke of being cultivated by horse-drawn machinery for centuries. Along the far end of the old meadow flowed the River Thames, barely twenty feet wide, pulling long wavy green weeds under a wooden foot-bridge. Blue-grey paint flaked off the handrail on the bridge whose underneath was overtaken by moss nourished on the damp air. We crossed the river and walked along the far bank where dry curved leaves had drifted under the willows in eddies. Near the village we climbed over a stone stile and looked back at the river in the gathering mist. The coping-stones on the dry-stone wall were speckled with a different, orange lichen.

I said goodbye to Claire outside the Lion Inn, where we finally tracked down the taxi driver. Travelling back to London on the train I thought about her magnificent boldness. If beauty is truth, the person who makes no attempt to hide their bad skin must be beautiful. I remembered Fritz of Fuck-Up Corner with tufts of hair sticking out of his mottled neck wandering around the lobby of the hotel at the Dead Sea, smiling and waving and being so friendly to complete strangers. That was beauty. Claire with her head held high was more gorgeous than any woman with uniformly smooth skin and a confident smile. She was actually better looking because she had psoriasis. Like Fritz, she was no longer going to hide behind hair, make-up, clothes, her hand, a book, or newspaper or scarf. She was saying: 'THIS IS TRULY WHO I AM' – the boldest and most beautiful statement any of us can make. And the harder it is to say, the more beautiful the person who says it must be.

Psoriasis is not something attached to me – it's part of me. I have other bits I'd prefer not to have, like my watery grey eyes, and my occasionally crazy behaviour, but I don't think of them as a disease that must be cured. Psoriasis is my natural state, and I must permit its imperfection, as I permit other imperfections. If I can believe this, and act on it, I would be cured, not of psoriasis, but of my war with my skin and myself. The ticket collector shuffled his way up the carriage towards me, and I met his eyes, knowing that after Claire's lunch I had a red bump between my eyes and flares of red skin on my left upper cheek and the tip of my nose. I looked into his eyes, and enjoyed – just for a scary moment – looking like the person I am, and being at peace with myself.

I got back home. The lights were off. I went to my desk and checked my email. There was one from Claire.

'Thanks for coming for lunch. It went rather well, didn't you think? I rather like being a mummy. I found the poem. Love Claire.'

Glory be to God for dappled things –
For skies of couple-colour as a brinded cow;
For rose-moles all in stipple upon trout that swim;
Fresh-firecoal chestnut-falls; finches' wings;

Landscape plotted and pieced – fold, fallow, and
plough;
And áll trádes, their gear and tackle and trim.

All things counter, original, spare, strange;
Whatever is fickle, freckled (who knows how?)
With swift, slow; sweet, sour; adazzle, dim;
He fathers-forth whose beauty is past change:
Praise him.

Acknowledgements

To make my adventures with my skin readable I have taken great liberties with time, place and identities. In addition, all names have been changed to protect identities. Every scene I describe I either observed or was told about by a reliable person, but I have often changed their locations, and sometimes their sequence. I have squeezed two or sometimes three people's experiences into a single character and have therefore moved people around the world and stretched or conflated their stories. If I hadn't, the book would have been a tedious 900 pages.

This book has been a long time in the making and I want to thank all those people who have helped it on its way: Claire Conville, Andy Miller, Francis Bickmore, Katherine Stanton and especially Stan Stanton, my brilliant agent. I would also like to thank my sisters Emma and Jane, my brother David and my mother and stepfather Susie and Stanley for helping me through it all. Thanks also to Edwin Tattum, Michael Israel and Bobby B for good times on the roof, and to Juliet and Britta Braun for many elucidating conversations in the lobby. Many thanks also to Mark Henriques, Jay Jopling and Dave Lee for always telling it like it is. Most importantly, I want to save my deepest gratitude for Ella, James and Portia, who have always loved and helped me, and who have been constant inspirations and the best of companions in good times and in bad. I love you all. Give thanks and praises.

To exchange information and views about this book visit www.sunbathingnaked.co.uk or to contact Guy Kennaway email sunbathingnaked@googlemail.co.uk.